Just over a year ago I outlined what was to be my major task as Minister for Health, the drawing up of a comprehensive Health Strategy.

I said then that the Strategy would have a clearly stated philosophy and clear and unequivocal objectives and targets including the necessary legislative measures to back them up. I am happy to say that this document delivers on this commitment and sets out a vision for the future of our health services which is both ambitious and pragmatic.

The primary aim of the Department of Health and the health services should be to enhance the health and quality of life of people.

In the absence of a clear strategic direction it is all too easy to lose sight of this fundamental purpose. The main theme of the Health Strategy is the reorientation or reshaping of our health services so that improving peoples' health and quality of life becomes the primary and unifying focus of all our efforts.

The document sets out three principles which underpin the entire Strategy: equity, quality of service and accountability.

Health policy, I believe, unerringly reveals the values that drive a society and the commitment of Governments to social justice. In giving prominence to the principle of equity the Strategy reflects my own personal commitment and that of the Government to ensuring that our health services should help first and foremost those people whose needs are greatest. Through the creation for the first time of health development sectors, the Government is sending a very clear signal about the way in which resources are to be allocated and directed in the future.

The concept of measuring quality has only begun to take hold in the healthcare area in recent years. The Strategy recognises the importance of the pursuit of quality at all levels of the service. It lays emphasis on constantly measuring and evaluating quality through clinical audit and consumer surveys. The Strategy firmly places the consumer first and sets out proposals for improved participation in the planning and evaluation of services.

In a service which costs two and a quarter billion pounds to run each year, now more than ever there is a need to demonstrate effectiveness and value for money for the taxpayer. The Strategy sets out new arrangements for improved legal and financial accountability. It includes a requirement on those providing the services to take direct responsibility for the achievement of agreed objectives.

In setting explicit objectives and targets particularly in the area of health promotion and prevention, the Strategy provides for the first time an agenda to shape a healthier Ireland. The Four Year Action Plan which accompanies the Strategy sets out specific developments across a range of services and actions to improve linkages between community based and acute hospital services in particular.

Recognising that our existing organisational structures are in many ways incapable of achieving this agenda for change, the Government has decided on a range of organisational reforms. These reforms will ensure that both my Department and the new health authorities will have the capacity to drive and implement the Strategy in the coming years.

The effective implementation of the Strategy is however not just a matter of legislation or resource allocation at a national level.

The reorientation proposed in this document is dependent on the support and enthusiasm of those who provide the services, the more than 60,000 staff working in the community, in hospitals and health boards all over the country.

We are extremely fortunate in the quality and commitment of our health service personnel in Ireland. Very few health systems are, I believe, better equipped to take on the challenge of working towards measurable health and social gain.

I believe that in the coming years this document will be seen as marking a new era for our health services. Particularly for the staff who provide the services, I hope it will help sustain and strengthen the sense of shared purpose and pride in being part of an effective and respected service for the people of Ireland.

Brendan Howlin TD
Minister for Health

Chapter one

Starting Points

Chapter two

The Services

Chapter three

The Framework

Chapter four

The Participants

Chapter five

The Next Steps

Shaping a healthier future

A strategy for effective healthcare in the 1990s

Dublin: Published by the Stationery Office

To be purchased through any Bookseller, or direct from the Government Publications Sales Office, Sun Alliance House, Molesworth St., Dublin 2.

(Pn. 0658)   **£5.00**   ISBN: 0-7076-0374-9

DEPARTMENT OF HEALTH
AN ROINN SLÁINTE

Four-Year Action Plan 1994-1997

Contents

The main theme of
the Health Strategy is the
reorientation of the system
by reshaping the way

services are

planned and

delivered.

An overview

The Irish people attach a high value to good health services. They expect to have access to health services when needed and to receive the highest standards of medical and nursing care. They believe that Government should fund caring services for those with disabilities, protect children from abuse and work to create an environment that promotes healthy living. Successive generations of Irish men and women, in the statutory and voluntary sectors, have worked hard to overcome diseases that maimed or killed prematurely, to guarantee access to services on the basis of need and to care for the ill and disabled in a way which respects their individuality and humanity. By international standards, we can be proud of the

Chapter one

Starting Points

comprehensive nature of our health and personal social services as well as the reputation for competence and compassion of those who have made their careers in the health services. These are substantial achievements; but there is a need to review periodically the direction in which services are developing and to redefine priorities. This document builds on the many strengths of the services while at the same time identifying the necessary directions for change.

The main theme of the Health Strategy is the reorientation of the system towards improving the effectiveness of the health and personal social services by reshaping the way that services are planned and delivered. There are three dimensions to this reorientation, each of which is examined in detail in the three chapters which follow. These are:

The Services

Prevention, treatment and care services will be more clearly focused on improvements in health status and the quality of life, and will place an increased emphasis on the provision of the most appropriate care.

The Framework

The management and organisational structures will provide for more decision-making and accountability at regional level, allied to better methods of performance measurement.

The Participants

There will be greater sensitivity to the right of the consumer to a service which responds to his or her needs in an equitable and quality-driven manner; and greater recognition will be given to the key role of those who provide the services and the importance of enabling them to do so to their full potential.

- The reorientation which will be brought about by the Health Strategy will affect the services for many years to come. Some of the changes will have an immediate impact, others will have a more gradual effect. Ultimately, these changes will radically transform the system as it moves into the twenty-first century.

- The reorientation is clearly, therefore, a long-term process. However, the period from now until 1997 will see major development and change in all aspects of the health and personal social services. The Strategy is accompanied by a Four-Year Action Plan which maps out the detail of what will be achieved.

- The Irish health services have evolved to encompass a wider range of responsibilities than in many other countries. In particular, they include a variety of personal social services directed towards supporting those who are dependent or disabled and protecting the welfare of the most vulnerable. While the term "the health services" is used for convenience throughout the Strategy, it should of course be understood to refer to the comprehensive range of services which they provide.

Ultimately, these changes will radically transform the system

The background

The system compares well

As a community, we provide for ourselves a healthcare system which compares well with other developed countries. The international experience is, in general, that countries as they become wealthier are prepared to devote more of their collective resources to supporting social expenditures in areas such as healthcare. In Ireland, however, we are already committing as high a **proportion** of our national wealth to healthcare as some countries which are significantly wealthier. The amount spent on healthcare **per capita** is, of course, considerably lower than in the more affluent countries.

This is not to imply that we are spending the 'wrong' amount on healthcare; it simply reflects a different order of national priorities in public spending. The strong commitment in Ireland to supporting health services may well derive from the long tradition of caring which has been intrinsic to our national character down the years.

Consolidation and efficiency

The recent history of the Irish health services reflects a period of consolidation of existing services and expansion in new areas to adapt to changing practices in treatment and care and to meet changing needs. The period has also been marked by a drive to extract maximum efficiency so that the volume and quality of patient services could be maintained at the greatest level possible at a time of very tight financial constraints.

Public Non-capital Health Expenditure 1984-1994

As a percentage of GNP

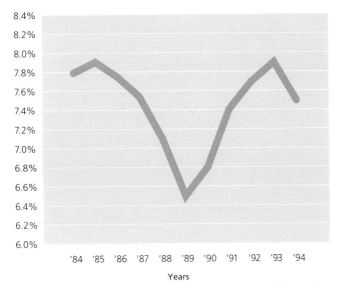

Government spending on healthcare as a percentage of GNP fell significantly in the period 1986-1989. However, with the improvement in the public finances in recent years this trend has been reversed and the share of GNP is now approaching the pre-1986 level.

Source *Department of Health*

A far-reaching response

However, a more far-reaching response is required to enable us to meet the challenges of the coming years. The demand for healthcare and personal social services is certain to increase rapidly, as is the cost of providing it. There are several reasons for this trend — our population is beginning to age, and the number of elderly people will rise significantly over the next ten to twenty years; the continuous development of health technology will expand the range of possible treatments.

We need to consider, as a community, how we intend to address these demands. It is quite clear that health spending has the potential to grow rapidly in response to the growing demands. In the past, when public spending was perceived to have grown too large relative to the capacity of the economy to support it, the adjustments required were dramatic and quite sudden in their effect. It is far preferable to analyse the challenges and opportunities ahead and to set out a planned approach to dealing with them, taking account of the fact that resources will inevitably be limited.

The context

Shaping a healthier future has not emerged in a vacuum. It must be seen in the context of the studies of the overall system and the reports on individual services over the last number of years. Among the key influences were *Health — The Wider Dimensions* (1986) and the *Report of the Commission on Health Funding* (1989). The many important sectoral reports have covered, for example, public health, general practitioner services, acute hospital services, mental and physical handicap, mental illness, the elderly, child care and many other areas. The publication of the various studies and reports has been followed by wide consultation with interested groups in relation to their implications. The development of the Strategy, particularly in relation to health promotion and the prevention of disease, has also taken account of the themes and targets of the World Health Organisation's "*Health for All*" programme, and of the potential for strengthening EU co-operation following the inclusion of responsibilities in this field in the Maastricht Treaty. The various studies and consultation processes have provided comprehensive analyses of our health services and the options for development and reform. These are now drawn together in a cohesive longer-term Strategy and Four-Year Action Plan. There will be further consultation with relevant groups in relation to the detailed implementation.

> ## The Strategy is accompanied by a Four-Year Action Plan

The strengths and weaknesses of the system

Our health system has many strengths which we can harness. These include:

- Services which are recognised internationally to be of high quality.

- Well-qualified, committed and caring staff trained to the best international standards.

- A strong voluntary sector which provides an integral part of the public system without forgoing the benefits of independence and flexibility.

- A mix of public and private services which facilitates complementary roles rather than conflict.

The Health Strategy is underpinned by the key principles of equity, quality of service and accountability

- A political and social consensus on the importance of an adequately funded, high-quality and equitable public system.

- A comprehensive planning framework offered by the in-depth studies of the system and of individual sectors carried out in recent years.

- There are inadequate linkages between complementary services, such as hospitals, general practitioners and other community services.

- Community-based services are not as yet developed to the extent that they can appropriately complement and substitute for institutional care, or provide adequately for those in the community who are dependent on support.

- The organisational and management structures, which are now in place for almost a quarter of a century, need to be updated to provide for more effective decision-making and accountability.

There are also, however, weaknesses which must be resolved so that the services can deliver to their full potential. In particular:

- Many of the services are not sufficiently focused towards specific goals or targets, and it is therefore difficult to assess their effectiveness; the information which would support this focusing is frequently unavailable or, if available, under-utilised.

- Insufficient attention has been paid to tackling the main causes of premature mortality, which results in lower life expectancy in Ireland than the EU average.

- The waiting times for certain services are too long.

The underlying principles

The Health Strategy is underpinned by a number of key principles.

Equity

The achievement of an equitable health service has a number of dimensions. Access to healthcare should be determined by actual need for services rather than ability to pay or geographic location. Formal entitlement to services is not enough; those needing services must have them available within a reasonable period. Furthermore, the pursuit of equity must extend beyond the question of access to treatment and care, and must examine variations in the health status of different groups in society and how these might be addressed.

Achieving equity in the healthcare system will involve not only ensuring fairness, but also being seen to be fair. The Strategy contains important steps to ensure greater equity in:

- Implementing uniform rules for eligibility and charges for services across the country

- Measures to reduce waiting-times for those availing of public services

- Giving special attention to certain disadvantaged groups

Population projections for the elderly to the year 2020

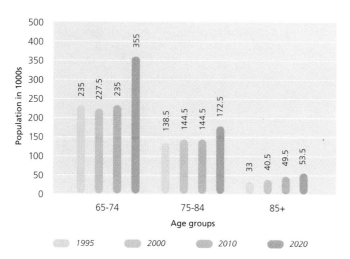

The number of persons aged over 65 is expected to grow by 40% in the next twenty five years. The number of persons aged over 85, where the likelihood of dependency on the health services is greatest, is expected to grow by 60%.

Source *Eurostat 1993 Demographic Statistics*
(average of projections made on alternative assumptions).

Quality of Service

The services must meet the highest possible quality standards within the resources that are available. This has two aspects:

- The technical quality of the treatment or care must be such that the best possible outcome is achieved in return for the resources which are committed to it. It is not sufficient to assess the services in terms of the volume of activity; a crucial element of the re-orientation is towards a more critical evaluation of the outcome of services through techniques such as clinical audit.

- The consumer's perception of the quality of the service he or she receives will be greatly influenced by factors such as the efficiency with which they are organised, the courtesy shown and the physical surroundings in which they are delivered. The maintenance of quality standards in these areas is also therefore of great importance.

Accountability

The principle of accountability has a number of strands. It includes formal legal and financial accountability arrangements, which are in place and which are subject to ongoing development. It also includes the requirement on those providing services to take explicit responsibility for the achievement of agreed objectives. This has been lacking in the health services, and its development is a key element of the Strategy's organisational and management reforms. Finally, there must also be mechanisms to ensure that those with decision-making powers are adequately accountable to the consumers of the services. This issue is also addressed in the Strategy.

Health expenditure as a share of GDP for 1991

Index of health expenditure per capita 1991 (USA = 100)

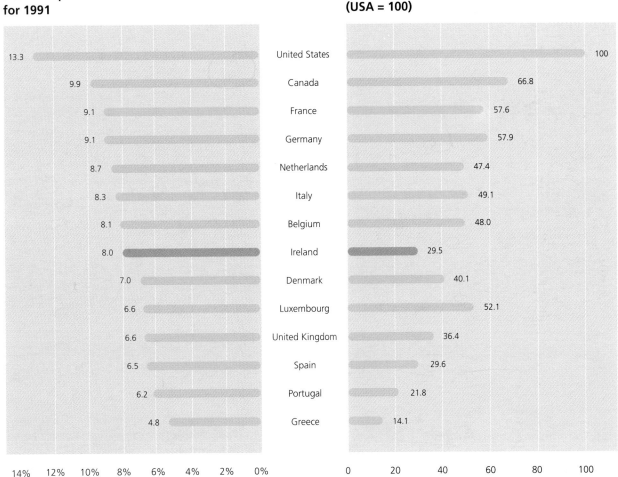

Country	Health expenditure as a share of GDP for 1991	Index of health expenditure per capita 1991 (USA = 100)
United States	13.3	100
Canada	9.9	66.8
France	9.1	57.6
Germany	9.1	57.9
Netherlands	8.7	47.4
Italy	8.3	49.1
Belgium	8.1	48.0
Ireland	8.0	29.5
Denmark	7.0	40.1
Luxembourg	6.6	52.1
United Kingdom	6.6	36.4
Spain	6.5	29.6
Portugal	6.2	21.8
Greece	4.8	14.1

Source *OECD Health Data*

Resources

Our ability to provide comprehensive and high-quality services is affected by both:

- The level of resources which can be made available

- The efficiency with which we use these resources

Ireland's expenditure on health and personal social services has, in recent years, averaged about 9 per cent of our Gross National Product. Of this, about 2 percent has been privately-financed, whether through voluntary health insurance or out-of-pocket expenditure; the publicly-financed element has averaged about 7 per cent of GNP. International comparisons compiled by the OECD exclude some elements of our health expenditure (such as the cost of income maintenance schemes) which are not regarded as health expenditure in other countries, and refer to the share of Gross Domestic Product rather than Gross National Product. On this standardised basis, health expenditure accounts for about 8 per cent of Ireland's GDP, a **share** which is broadly comparable to that for other EU countries. However, Ireland's **per capita** GDP is at the lower end of the range. Consequently, the amount of money spent on healthcare per person in Ireland, although it represents a major commitment of national resources, is considerably lower than that in the EU countries with which our services tend to be compared.

We have nonetheless succeeded in developing many services, particularly in acute hospitals, which are recognised as being on a par with those in considerably more affluent countries. The Four-Year Action Plan will require further investment, particularly in relation to the completion of the 1991-1997 programme for the development of community-based services which was first set out in the *Programme for Economic and Social Progress* and which has been included in the new *Programme for Competitiveness and Work.*

The Government will aim to provide over the next four years the resources for the development needs identified in the Action Plan which is incorporated in this Strategy, while observing the budgetary policy set out in its Programme for a Partnership Government. The amount which can be made available in any given year will have to be decided by the Government in the context of its financial position and its other public expenditure priorities at that time.

Regardless of the level of resources which can be made available, we need to look more closely at how we use them. It will be clear throughout the Health Strategy that a central element in the planned reshaping of the services is the emphasis which will in future be placed on achieving the greatest possible benefit from whatever resources are available.

The change
of emphasis
which will
result from
this Health
Strategy will transform the
basis upon which choices
are made.

The health and personal social services are directed towards:

Health promotion and disease prevention
Promoting good health, reducing preventable illness and increasing life expectancy.

Treatment
Providing appropriate responses to illness when it arises.

Continuing care
Supporting those who are dependent or disabled and protecting the welfare of the most vulnerable. These are, of course, very broad statements of the overall tasks, and the objectives of the individual

Chapter two
The **Services**

services can be expressed in more detailed terms. However, these objectives have tended until now to focus on the provision of a **level of service** rather than on the provision of a **positive outcome**. For example, the performance of the hospital service has tended to be measured in terms of the number of patients treated rather than in terms of its effectiveness in dealing with their illnesses. This arises, of course, because of the difficulties in measuring the benefits concerned, and these difficulties are even greater in the case of services directed at ongoing support and care rather than treatment and cure.

Nonetheless, data and analytical tools are now available which permit far better evaluation than was previously possible of the needs which the services must address and their effectiveness in doing so.

Health gain: achieving improvements in health

Social gain: adding to the quality of life

This Chapter explains how the concepts of **health gain** and **social gain**, allied to greatly improved data collection and analysis, will be used to focus the prevention, treatment and care services more clearly on improvements in health status or the quality of life. It also addresses another element in the reorientation of services — an increased emphasis on the provision of **the most appropriate care**, which in turn requires the improvement of the **linkages** between services. Finally, it considers the longer-term challenge of finding ways to involve the public in general in the priority-setting process.

The detailed short-term plans for the individual services, on foot of the approach set out in the Strategy, are contained in the accompanying Four-Year Action Plan.

Health gain and social gain

A benefit or outcome

Health gain and social gain are terms used to indicate that patients and clients of the health or personal social services should receive a clear benefit (or outcome) from their contact with the system.

Health gain is concerned with health status, both in terms of increases in life expectancy and in terms of improvements in the quality of life through the cure or alleviation of an illness or disability or through any other general improvement in the health of the individual or the population at whom the service is directed.

Social gain is concerned with broader aspects of the quality of life. It includes, for example, the quality added to the lives of dependent elderly people and their carers as a result of the provision of support services, or the benefit to a child of living in an environment free of physical and psychological abuse.

Both health gain and social gain are concerned with focusing on the value that can be added to a person's life, whether in the form of a short-term treatment or an intervention required for a longer period. Both concepts underline the need for a demonstrable benefit from the health services, while recognising that the benefit in question may not be easily measured. It is important to stress that these concepts do not imply that services whose outcomes are more easily measurable should have precedence over those where the benefits are less tangible. However, the emphasis in all services should be on the application of resources in whatever way will yield the most benefit.

Transforming the basis of choice

Choices on the use of resources are made every day at all levels of the services. There are not, and could never be, sufficient resources to meet all the needs which can be identified. Choices are made at a national level, in deciding on the funding to be allocated to particular regions and to particular programmes. The process of decision-making continues at each successive level, right down to the individual doctor or community worker who has to prioritise the relative needs of individual patients or clients. The change of emphasis which will result from the Health Strategy is about transforming the basis upon which choices are made. The need for such a transformation was highlighted by the Commission on Health Funding which argued as follows:

These choices will reflect the relative priorities accorded by government to the competing demands of society. However, the efficiency of the health services will be increased to the extent that these priorities, and the choices which they determine, are based on an evaluation of the health-care needs of the population and of the relative effectiveness of the available responses to different forms of need. Such an approach places considerable emphasis on data collection and analysis. Its advantage is that, despite our often limited understanding of the effects of healthcare, it provides some objective basis for how we allocate resources. Otherwise, choices will continue to be made in an arbitrary way and mainly in the interests of those groups able to exert the most influence on the resource allocation process.

Commission on Health Funding (1989) Para 5.8.

It is clear that comprehensive and good quality information is an essential prerequisite for the application of this approach — information on needs, information on activity, information on detailed costs and information on outcomes.

The implications of the health gain and social gain concepts for the different categories of services are now considered.

Health promotion and disease prevention

The starting point

Health promotion provides the obvious starting point for any refocusing of the health services towards improving health status and the quality of life.

Very good progress has been made in improving the health of our population as a whole in recent decades. For example:

- Life expectancy in Ireland has increased substantially. Since 1950 life expectancy at birth has increased by 11 years for women and by 8 years for men.

- There has been a dramatic drop in infant mortality. The death rate among infants has fallen from 68 per 1,000 live births in 1947 to just 8 per 1,000 in 1991.

- Childhood vaccination programmes have had a major impact upon communicable diseases.

- The death rate from strokes has almost halved since 1972 and there has also been a significant reduction in deaths from heart disease.

- Mortality from road traffic accidents, other accidents and poisoning has shown a welcome drop in recent years.

However, this is not the full picture; much remains to be done to achieve the objective of improving our health status still further. For instance, over one-fifth of all deaths in Ireland in 1992 were of people aged less than 65. This is premature mortality and much of it is preventable. While good progress has been made, there is still room for improvement.

We have high premature mortality rates — much of it is preventable

Life expectancy at birth

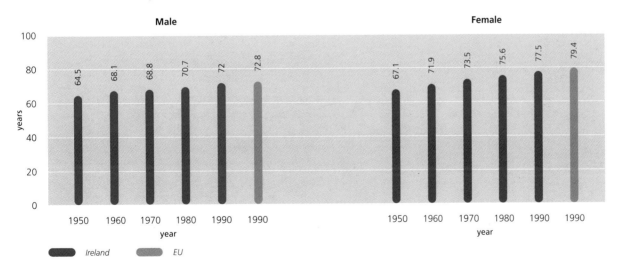

Life expectancy has improved greatly over the last forty years but is below the EU average

Source *CSO and Eurostat*

Infant mortality
Rate per 1,000 live births

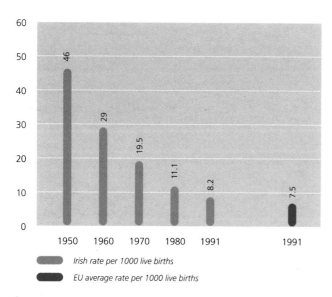

Legend:
- Irish rate per 1000 live births
- EU average rate per 1000 live births

Infant mortality has fallen very dramatically and is now close to the EU average

Source *CSO and Eurostat*

Accidents
Death rate per 100,000 population

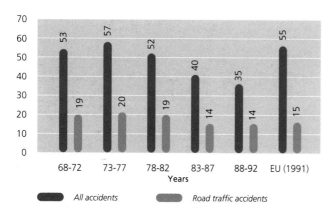

Legend:
- All accidents
- Road traffic accidents

There has been a marked drop in deaths from road traffic accidents and from accidents in general. Both rates are below the EU average.

Source *CSO, Eurostat and WHO (Age – standardised data)*

Deaths from heart attack and stroke
Death rate per 100,000 population

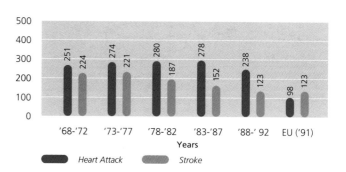

Legend:
- Heart Attack
- Stroke

While death rates from heart attack have been falling they are still above the EU average. However, the death rate from stroke has fallen dramatically to the EU average.

Source *CSO, Eurostat and WHO (Age – standardised data)*

Cancer mortality
Death rate per 100,000 population

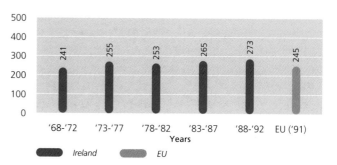

Legend:
- Ireland
- EU

The death rate from cancer is rising and is above the EU average.

Source *CSO, Eurostat and WHO (Age – standardised data)*

Lung cancer mortality
Death rate per 100,000 population

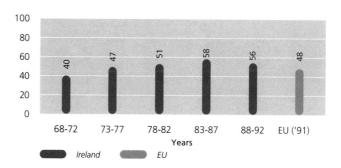

Legend:
- Ireland
- EU

The death rate from lung cancer has started to fall but remains above the EU average.

Source *CSO, Eurostat and WHO (Age – standardised data)*

Causes of premature mortality in 1992

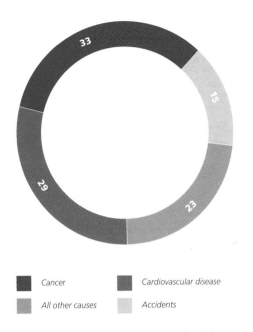

- Cancer
- Cardiovascular disease
- All other causes
- Accidents

Cancer, cardiovascular disease and accidents account for the majority of deaths among persons under 65

Source *CSO*

Life expectancy Life expectancy at birth is still below that for most other countries in the EU. On 1991 figures, Ireland ranks 11th out of the twelve countries for women and 9th for men.

Much of the improvement in life expectancy at birth, which was mentioned above, arises from better health and social provisions for infants and young children. Life expectancy in middle age has increased only slightly in recent years and compares poorly with our EU neighbours — Irish women rank lowest and men second lowest in this regard at age 40.

Heart disease, strokes and circulatory disorders accounted for almost one-third of all premature deaths in 1992. These conditions can be influenced by lifestyle (such as diet, exercise and smoking). While deaths from heart disease have been falling they are still above the EU average.

Cancer Death rates from cancer have risen slightly in recent years and account for one-third of all premature deaths. Our rates are above the average of our EU counterparts. Lung cancer is the most common type in Ireland and accounted for a growing number of deaths until around 1987. While it has fallen since then,

it compares unfavourably with the EU average. Breast cancer accounts for about 10 per cent of the deaths of women aged under 65.

Smoking Despite our preventive strategies, smoking-related disease still causes over 6,000 deaths in Ireland every year. The incidence of smoking has declined from 43 per cent of adults in the early 1970s to 28 per cent today, but it remains the chief cause of premature death, including 90 per cent of those from lung cancer. A worrying trend is the increasing number of women — 500 in 1992 — who die from lung cancer.

Weight problems About two-thirds of adult men and nearly half of adult women are overweight according to a national nutrition survey published in 1990. The Kilkenny Health Project found that almost one quarter of people in their survey aged between 35 and 64 had high blood pressure. There is a recognised link between being overweight and having high blood pressure, high cholesterol, diabetes and cardio-vascular disease.

Alcohol misuse We continue to have a serious problem with alcohol misuse. Almost one-quarter of admissions to psychiatric hospitals are related to alcohol. The degree of alcohol misuse among young people is causing growing concern and alcohol remains a key factor contributing to road accidents.

Regional blackspots There is evidence in individual regions of some 'black spots' where mortality rates are higher than the countrywide average, due mainly to factors such as unemployment, high-stress living or working conditions and inadequate access to needed services.

Groups with special needs There is also evidence of health inequalities in groups with special needs such as travellers. This group has a much higher death rate from heart disease, cancer, respiratory conditions, congenital abnormalities and accidents. In turn this results in significantly lower life expectancy for travellers — ten years less for men and twelve for women — compared to the population overall.

Indicators such as the above have been used to identify the aspects of health promotion to be given priority in the Health Strategy. The overall objective under this heading is to improve life expectancy so as to move over time to the higher levels being enjoyed in a number of EU countries. This involves concentrating in particular on the three main causes of premature mortality in Ireland:

- Cardiovascular disease

- Cancer

- Accidents

Cardiovascular disease (i.e. heart disease, strokes and circulatory disorders) and cancer each account for about one-third of deaths of people under 65. In addition to those who die prematurely as a result of these conditions, many others suffer ill-health and reductions in their quality of life. Accidents account for about 15 per cent of deaths in that age-group, but about one-third of deaths of people under 45; again, many people who survive accidents suffer ongoing illness or disability as a result. In addition to the human costs of these premature illnesses, disabilities and deaths, there are, of course, very heavy financial costs to the health services which, if they could be reduced, would make more resources available to meet the many other priority needs. Each of these causes of premature death is influenced by risk factors which can be tackled by appropriate initiatives. The approach in the Health Strategy is therefore:

- To set a medium-term target for the reduction of premature mortality due to each of these causes.

- To set very specific targets related to the relevant risk factors (such as, for example, a given reduction in the proportion of the population who smoke).

- To implement programmes designed to achieve the targets.

- To monitor the impact of the programmes on the targeted indicators.

While the medium term targets are expressed in terms of reductions in death rates in the under-65 age group, the beneficial impact of the programmes will also be seen, over time, in life expectancy at age 65 and beyond.

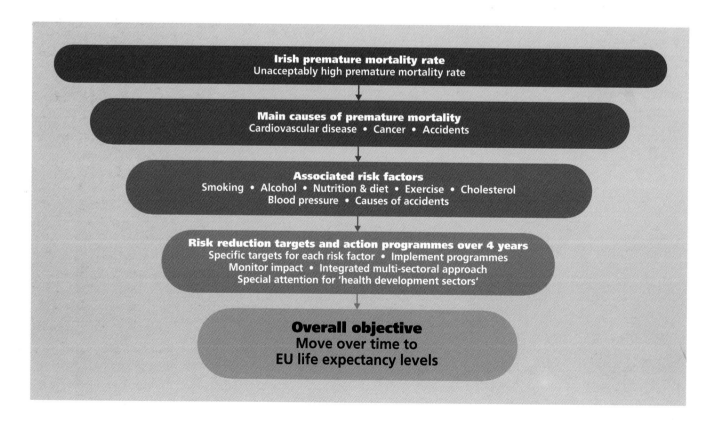

Cardiovascular disease

It is estimated that smoking is the cause of about 30 per cent of cardiovascular deaths internationally. Cardiovascular disease is also influenced significantly by factors such as diet and blood cholesterol level. Other risk factors include hypertension, high alcohol consumption and lack of physical exercise. **The medium-term target is to reduce the death rate from cardiovascular disease in the under-65 age group by 30 per cent in the next ten years.** This compares with the reduction of about 30 per cent which was achieved over the last twenty years.

Cancer

Smoking is a critical risk factor in the incidence of cancer. It is a major causative factor in almost 90 per cent of the 1,500 deaths from lung cancer which occur in Ireland each year. It is also known to increase the risk of cancers of the mouth, throat, oesophagus, bladder and kidneys. Studies have also suggested that consumption of animal fat is positively related to the risk of cancer while increased fibre consumption may reduce this risk. Over-exposure to sunlight is an increasing cause of skin cancers. **The medium-term target is to reduce the death rate from cancer in the under-65 age-group by 15 per cent in the next ten years.** This compares with the reduction of about 7 per cent which has been achieved over the last twenty years. The latter reduction is disappointing in view of the preventable nature of much cancer, especially lung cancer. The recent experience therefore suggests that the target is an ambitious one. It is not unachievable but will clearly require an intensification of the programmes directed towards the prevention of cancer.

Accidents

Road traffic accidents are by far the most common cause of accidental deaths, and the risk factors include alcohol consumption, road and vehicle safety and driver behaviour. Accidental deaths and injuries also arise as a result of reducible risk factors in the home, in the workplace and in leisure activities. There has been a welcome decreasing trend in accidental deaths which, across age-groups as a whole, fell by about 37 per cent over the past twenty years. This level of reduction is broadly similar to the rate of decline which was set by the World Health Organisation as a target in the mid-1980s i.e. a reduction of at least 25 per cent by the year 2000, and may provide a basis for setting an appropriate medium-term target now. However, given the multi-sectoral approach and concerted action required to achieve accident reduction, such a target is not being specified at this stage but will be developed during 1994 following consultations with all the relevant Departments and agencies.

The risk reduction targets and action programmes, which are detailed in the accompanying Four-Year Action Plan, will focus on six key areas:

- **Smoking**
- **Alcohol**
- **Nutrition and diet**
- **Exercise**
- **Cholesterol and blood pressure**
- **Causes of accidents**

Guiding principles

The targets have been set according to the following guiding principles:

- They are realistic and attainable within the time frame set for them.

- They are measurable so that progress in attaining them can be monitored.

- They are framed nationally, but with a view to local targets being developed in line with the needs of the region. It is crucial that the national targets are complemented by targets which the region concerned sets and implements.

The monitoring of progress in relation to these targets will be a crucial part of the Strategy. There is little point in setting a range of targets, whether national or local, if information is not available with which to monitor their implementation. **A comprehensive data base will be developed.** This will provide detailed information on areas such as smoking, alcohol consumption, use of drugs, diet and nutrition, level of fitness and stress. This is essential if plans and programmes are to be targeted effectively. It will enable planners to:

- Assess both nationally and locally the factors upon which health promotion needs to focus.

- Develop appropriate responses to those factors in accordance with the identified priorities.

- Monitor progress at national and local level in implementing the programmes and achieving the targets that have been set.

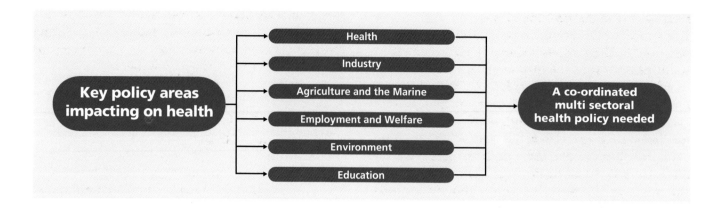

A multi-sectoral approach

It is important also to place health promotion in a wider context. The activities of many other sectors have an impact on health, and it is essential therefore that there is a health dimension to public policies in areas such as industry, agriculture, education and the environment. There is an increased emphasis, both nationally and internationally, on the multi-sectoral approach to health promotion, and this is now an integral part of EU policy as set out in Article 129 of the Maastricht Treaty. The role of the health services in influencing policy developments in other sectors, and in liaising closely with the relevant agencies, will become more significant.

The Four-Year Action Plan which accompanies the Health Strategy sets out the detailed targets for the various programmes and describes the scope for co-operation and joint action both with other sectors and within the EU. Later in 1994, a comprehensive Health Promotion Strategy will be published which will provide more detail on the targets and on the programmes for their achievement.

Community health services

The health services provide a wide range of other programmes directed at preventing illness and improving health status. These include:

- Programmes to prevent the spread of communicable diseases.

- Programmes to improve dental and oral health.

- Programmes to identify and treat conditions and defects in young children.

- Food and medicine controls.

- Specific services targeting at-risk groups.

These will also be focused more directly on the achievement of measurable improvements in health status. Targets for these programmes are also set out in the Four-Year Action Plan.

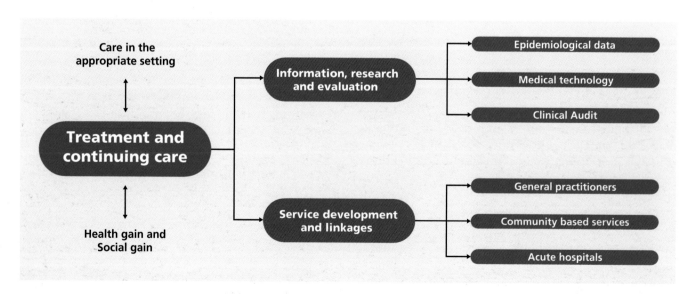

Health development sectors

The principle of equity imposes a particular obligation upon the health services to pay special attention to geographic areas or population groups (such as travellers) where the indicators of health status are below average. Most of the causal factors, such as poverty and unemployment, are outside the direct control of the health services. However, much can still be done to improve health status through tailoring and organising the delivery of health education programmes and community services to take account of the needs of the target groups. Examples of possible approaches include giving priority to disadvantaged areas in deciding the location of Health Centres; developing "Community Mother" programmes to support mothers in need of assistance and advice; and designing health promotion programmes specifically for the groups concerned.

Under the Health Strategy, there will be a specific policy of targeting resources towards areas or groups with low health status and giving them priority in the development of services. The health boards will be required to identify "health development sectors" in each region on the basis of indicators of health status and social problems. Priorities will be reordered to support pilot schemes which will target programmes at these sectors and evaluate their effectiveness over time in terms of improvements in the indicators.

The health boards will be encouraged to adopt varying approaches in their pilot schemes, and the approaches which prove most effective can then be adopted for similar target groups or areas elsewhere.

Treatment and continuing care

While the increased emphasis on health promotion is crucial to the Health Strategy, it is of course the case that the vast bulk of the resources available to the health services are devoted to the treatment of illness and the support of those who need ongoing care.

General practitioners are, in most cases, the first point of contact with the healthcare system and are a key component of it. Significant progress has been made in recent years in the development of general practice; however, it suffers from a degree of isolation from the rest of the system which must be addressed if its full potential is to be achieved.

Our **acute hospital system** compares favourably with international standards. However, with changing needs and changing technologies, its processes and its relationship with the rest of the system need constant reassessment.

The **continuing care** services are in a process of rapid development. In particular, community-based services are being provided both as an alternative to institutional care where appropriate and to address previously unmet needs for support for vulnerable groups.

The thrust of the Health Strategy, for these and for the wide range of other elements of the health and personal social services, is to ensure that both national and local decision-making on the planning and the delivery of services are directed towards:

- **Achieving the greatest possible health gain or social gain for the resources that are available.**

- **Ensuring that the treatment or care is provided in the most appropriate setting.**

The second of these objectives is related to the first, since the benefits in terms of both health gain and social gain can be increased by providing services in a setting that is more appropriate to the patient's medical and other circumstances. This may involve providing community-based rather than institutional care for a person who can, as a result, continue to live at home; or it may mean providing the most appropriate option from a number of types of institutional care.

The measures which will be taken to achieve these objectives include:

- Providing better information, research and evaluation as a basis for decision making.

- Continuing the development of services, particularly in the community, which satisfy the criteria implied in the objectives.

- Strengthening the linkages between services to support the provision of appropriate care.

Information, research and evaluation

The application of the health gain and social gain concepts to the planning and delivery of services will rely very heavily on the collection and analysis of accurate and comprehensive data, as a basis for:

- Better identification of the needs to be addressed.

- Better evaluation of existing and new technology, and of alternative approaches to the delivery of services.

- Ongoing monitoring and evaluation of the effectiveness of services, taking both costs and outcomes into account.

Information gathering While broad epidemiological data is available at a national level, pilot work on local information systems has proven that there can be significant variations in health needs within relatively small areas. The Commission on Health Funding stressed the need for local information systems which would include comprehensive population registers with demographic and health profiles and data on morbidity and mortality. Much of the necessary raw data are already collected through the Hospital In-Patient Enquiry Scheme and through various surveys carried out by the Central Statistics Office, the National Cancer Registry, health agencies and other bodies, and computerised systems can be used to integrate these for analysis on an area basis. Priority will be given to the development of such information systems, with a key role being played by the Regional Departments of Public Health which will be established in each health board.

These systems will provide a basis for the identification of needs but will also be of benefit, when combined with data on costs and outcomes, in comparing alternative approaches to the delivery of care and in evaluating the effectiveness of services. Research into these issues will be given increased priority and funding at both local and national level. Research will also be directed towards improving the measurement of health gain and, in particular, developing approaches to the measurement of social gain.

Evaluating technology The term medical technology is often associated with equipment, but its true meaning embraces all methods of providing treatment to patients. Recent developments in high-technology medicine, all of which have been extremely costly, include diagnostic machines such as magnetic resonance imaging equipment, chemotherapeutic drugs and highly-skilled minimally invasive surgical techniques such as laparoscopic surgery.

The introduction of new medical technologies into the health services here and in other countries continues to accelerate. There has been a general tendency, here as elsewhere, for new technologies to spread rapidly before there has been any systematic appraisal of their costs and benefits. This can arise from the understandable desire of doctors and patients to make use of any developments which offer the prospect of better and more effective care. However, many countries have now turned away from an unquestioning acceptance of new technology, and have introduced formal systems of appraisal.

As part of the Health Strategy, a formal system of technology assessment will be introduced. An advisory committee will be appointed to consider what type of assessment system is best suited to a small country such as ours.

Clinical audit A structured programme of clinical audit is fundamental to the provision of quality healthcare. Clinical audit is the systematic review of the manner in which healthcare is provided — from the individual's first point of contact with the service through to an assessment of the outcome of the care which he or she received. All health professionals contributing to patient care fall within the scope of this process. The promotion of clinical audit will be centred on the following principles:

- Guidelines and protocols cannot be imposed from on high. Practitioners must be involved in their development and stand over their implementation.

- It must be multi-disciplinary and have the backing of representative and teaching bodies. It must also take into account the patient's perspective on the outcome and quality of his or her care.

- It must be seen as an integral and routine part of healthcare, not as an exceptional or optional item. To this end, the results of clinical audit programmes must feed back into the service to give improved quality of care for patients.

> A programme of action to support and promote clinical audit will be drawn up through discussions with the various parties involved, which will commence in the coming months.
>
> The programme will be based on the principles outlined above and will take account of the many existing local initiatives in this area.

Service development

A complex range of services The health and personal social services are subject to rapid change and development, in response to very many factors. Demographic trends and changing patterns of illness and disease affect health needs, while technological advances can have a dramatic impact on the methods of dealing with them. The approaches to supporting those in need of continuing care are adapted over time to reflect the changing consensus on what form of care is of most benefit, and to respond to previously unmet needs. Problems in society as a whole, such as crime, family violence and unemployment lead in turn to a need for new and expanded personal social services. The range and complexity of the services provided under the aegis of the healthcare system is now very much greater than was the case even ten or twenty years ago.

An ongoing process of change That rapid change and development has taken place is not in doubt. The acute hospital service has been streamlined to meet changing needs. This has meant the closure of some older hospitals with the transfer of their services to more modern facilities. Developments over recent years in medical treatments and surgical techniques have led to a major shift in the nature of the services which the acute hospitals provide. Through the introduction of new treatment procedures such as day surgery, and reduced lengths of stay due to improved technology, the quality of service has been improved and the level of activity, in terms of the number of patients treated, has been maintained. Significant progress has been made in developing a network of community-based services to provide an alternative to institutional care and to enable those who are dependent on support due to infirmity or disability to retain their independence and to achieve an acceptable quality of life.

It is not suggested that these developments have taken place in the absence of appropriate research and evaluation. On the contrary, great reliance has been placed on the work of various advisory bodies and study groups, whose findings have been particularly influential, for example, in shaping the programme of development of community-based services. Nor is it necessary to have sophisticated measurement systems to demonstrate that significant social gain is achieved by tackling many of the areas of pressing need which are being addressed under the latter programme. However, we are now reaching the stage of development where the priorities for further attention need more rigorous evaluation.

> The accompanying Four-Year Action Plan sets out comprehensive development plans for the individual services on foot of the direction and underlying principles of the Strategy.

Planning for health and social gain In focusing the programmes towards health gain and social gain, account has been taken of the best available information and analysis at a national level of the needs to be addressed and the most effective ways of doing so. The programmes will require the preparation of detailed implementation plans at local level, again based on the best available information and evaluation. This is an incremental process. The information and analysis systems are being improved but decisions on the development of services clearly cannot be postponed until this process is complete. The information now available provides a far better basis for decision-making than was previously the case, and the thrust of the Strategy will be to continue to refine this process.

The programmes have also been designed to meet the objective of providing care in the most appropriate setting. This gives an obvious impetus to the development of community based services but also affects the shape of the hospital system and its relationship with other services. In relation to hospital services, the role of each hospital will be defined as part of a co-ordinated network of services delivering high-quality care in the appropriate setting, in an equitable and cost-effective manner. The growing complexity of hospital treatment and the continuing trend towards day care must also be taken into account; these and other factors will have implications for the organisation and delivery of the hospital services, including the physical planning and operational policies of new or replacement facilities.

The development of other services, particularly those in the community, will continue to gather momentum. In particular, it will be a requirement on health boards that their detailed implementation plans in respect of community services should be prepared on the basis of appropriate local catchment areas.

Linkages between services

The system is too compartmentalised To achieve the objective of providing care in an appropriate setting, it is essential that there are effective linkages between the services. Hospitals, general practitioners and other community services should operate as elements of an integrated system within which patients can move freely as their needs dictate. At present, the system is too compartmentalised to permit this flexibility.

Linking GPs and hospitals General practitioners, as independent contractors, have traditionally operated separately from the other community-based services and have had inadequate links with the acute hospitals. However, a blueprint for developing general practice, which was agreed with the medical organisations in 1992, stressed the need for integration with the rest of the system. The promotion of these links has been given impetus by the establishment of general practice units in each health board. These include general practice medical officers who are in active practice in their local areas. The units are therefore in an ideal position to develop closer contact and better working relationships between general practitioners and the other health and social services. At the hospital level, there will be an increased emphasis on the provision to general practitioners of an appropriate referral service.

Linking community care and hospitals There has also been a significant problem in relation to the lack of integration between services for the elderly in the community and those in hospitals. Dependent or ill elderly people need a range of services in and outside of hospitals which must be properly co-ordinated. Failure to do so can lead to the unnecessary admission to hospital of patients who could have been treated in the community. The lack of co-ordination has arisen partly from fragmentation in the organisation of services, and this is addressed in the planned reorganisation which is discussed in the next chapter. However, it can also be addressed by the provision of certain services which provide the necessary linkages, such as specialist departments of old age in general hospitals.

> It is a key objective of this Strategy to ensure that better linkages are forged between the various services. The accompanying Four-Year Action Plan includes a number of measures in relation to general practitioners, acute hospitals and services for the elderly which are designed to strengthen these linkages.

Broadening the priority-setting process

Open and objective

One of the central themes running through this chapter is that decisions on priorities and the allocation of resources will be made in a more open and objective way and will draw in particular on detailed information and analysis of needs, costs and outcomes. However, the priority-setting process can never be made entirely objective. One can establish the potential benefits to be derived from different types of services, but a subjective decision still needs to be made in relation to the relative value of these benefits.

For example, it may be possible to measure the health gain deriving from cardiac surgery and from joint replacements; it may be possible to measure the social gain deriving from better support services for the parents of children with mental handicap living in the community — but how are these quite different benefits to be ranked in determining where extra resources are to be made available?

As the Commission on Health Funding pointed out, there is a tendency for such choices to be made in an arbitrary way and mainly in the interests of those groups able to exert the most influence on the resource allocation process. This is very much in conflict with the principle of equity.

Identifying the preferences of the public

The decisions on priorities must, of course, be taken by the Government. However, it would assist the decision-making process if it was possible to devise some means of identifying and informing the preferences of the public in general between alternative priorities. A number of countries and international organisations have been examining possible ways of doing so. We can draw from their investigations and discussions, but it is ultimately a matter for ourselves to decide whether it is possible to develop any method for seeking a broadly-based national consensus on what our priorities should be.

This is a difficult challenge, and it would be foolish and misleading to pretend that clear answers are likely to be easily found. However, any progress which we can make towards discussing our healthcare priorities at a national level will, at the very least, provide some assistance to the decision-making process.

It will be an important part of the Health Strategy over the coming years to reorientate the decision-making process towards more open and explicit choice mechanisms which take account not only of detailed information and analysis, but which also strive to reflect the public's preferences to whatever degree is possible. The question of how the latter objective is to be achieved will require extensive consideration and discussion.

To begin this process, the Department of Health will initiate detailed research into possible app-roaches to identifying the public's preferences between competing priorities.

Assisting the decision making process

The framework must support the effective delivery of care.

Chapter two described the changes of emphasis which the prevention, treatment and care services will undergo in order to increase their effectiveness. However, the necessary changes go beyond the individual services. We must also examine the overall framework within which they operate, and ensure that it acts to support rather than hinder their effectiveness.

The main component of the framework is, of course, the organisational and management structure of the health services. The Government has accepted that major changes are now necessary to update this structure so that it supports the provision of effective care. This chapter describes these changes, which will require legislation, and explains their implications for the roles and responsibilities of the various levels of the structure.

Chapter three

The **Framework**

The eligibility structure and the role of the private sector are also important components of the framework. These are also addressed in this chapter.

Organisational structures

Our existing organisational structures date back over twenty years, to the Health Act, 1970, which established the health boards and defined their role in the provision of services. A number of reviews of the organisation of the health services have been carried out in recent years.

These reviews have been consistent in identifying certain key problems in the present structure. The Commission on Health Funding summarised them as follows:

- It confuses political and executive functions, and therefore undermines both.

- It fails to achieve a proper balance between national and local decision-making.

- The decision-making process does not provide a sufficient role for information and evaluation.

- Accountability within the structure is inadequate.

- There is insufficient integration of related services.

- There is inadequate effective representation of the interests of individual patients and clients within the structure.

While these deficiencies apply to the structure as a whole, there is a particular problem in the Eastern Health Board area. Here, to a greater extent than elsewhere, significant services are provided by voluntary agencies, but there is no single authority with an overall responsibility to co-ordinate all services and to ensure appropriate linkages between them. These organisational problems were highlighted in 1991 by the reports of both the Dublin Hospital Initiative Group and the Hospital Efficiency Review Group.

In 1991, the Government announced its intention to proceed with organisational reform so as to address these problems. Greater clarity would be brought to the roles, relationships and accountability of health board memberships, their Chief Executive Officers, the Minister and Department and the other agencies involved in the delivery of services. The Eastern Health Board would be replaced by a new authority which would have comprehensive responsibility for all health and personal social services in the Eastern region.

Having set out the broad principles of its proposals, the Government established a consultation process which produced a very comprehensive and positive response from over a hundred organisations and interested parties. The views put forward during this process have been taken into account in preparing the more detailed proposals which are set out below.

The purpose of changing the organisational and management structures is to support the provision of more effective care. It will therefore be of direct benefit to patients, clients and the wider community.

New legislation

Legislation will be introduced to provide for the new authority in the Eastern region and to remedy the deficiencies which have been identified in relation to all health boards. It will:

- Build on the strengths of the existing structure.

- Ensure that important decisions about regional services are taken at a regional level.

- Encourage community involvement in the organisation and delivery of services through the network of voluntary agencies.

The principles which will underpin the legislative proposals are:

- The Minister and Department should be responsible for the development of health policy and overall control of expenditure but should not be involved in the detailed management of the health services.

- Greater responsibility should be devolved to the appropriate executive agencies.

- The roles of all key parties, including the boards and managements of the statutory authorities, must be clearly defined.

- Greater autonomy must be balanced by increased accountability at all levels and there must be independent monitoring and evaluation of the performance of the executive agencies.

Key problems have been identified in the existing structure

The legislation will be general in nature and will provide a framework within which the statutory and voluntary agencies will operate. The more detailed day to day arrangements for putting this into effect, to be worked out later, will be sufficiently flexible to reflect local requirements.

Identifying roles and responsibilities

If the service is to be more responsive to the needs of patients and clients, decisions which affect their care must be taken as near to the point of service delivery as possible. It is essential that our organisational structures provide for the proper assignment of decision-making. Some decisions require to be taken at national level to ensure uniform access to services and for budgetary reasons. On the other hand, operational decisions are best taken locally, with local knowledge.

In addition to assigning decision-making to the appropriate level, it is also essential that the responsibilities of agencies and individuals at all levels are clearly stated and understood.

These essential requirements can only be achieved by changing some long-established relationships, between the Department and the statutory and voluntary agencies, between the health boards and the voluntary agencies, and within the health boards as well.

The regional health boards will be re-named as "health authorities" to emphasise the clearer distinction which will now be made between the respective roles and responsibilities of the board members and the management team.

Role of the Department of Health

While the Minister for Health will of course continue to have ultimate responsibility to the Oireachtas for all health services, his Department will no longer be involved in the detailed management of individual services. In addition to its roles in providing general support to the Minister for Health and preparing legislation, its principal responsibilities will be:

- Advising and supporting the Minister in determining national policy.

- Strategic planning and management at a national level.

- Advising the Minister for Health and the Government in its determination of the annual Health Estimate.

- Determining the financial allocation of the regional health authorities.

- Determining the overall personnel policies within which health authorities function.

- Monitoring and evaluating the service and financial performance of the authorities against national objectives and standards.

- Identifying and supporting the introduction of more effective management practices.

- Supporting the Minister in his functions in relation to other statutory bodies under his aegis.

Role of the health authorities

The division of health administration into eight regions has worked well since its introduction in 1971 and has provided a strong element of local democracy in the health services. The local populations now identify with the boards for their region, and the planning and delivery of services has evolved in that context. The problems which need to be addressed in relation to the management of the health services are not related to the number of boards and it is not proposed to change the present structure. There will, however, be crucial changes in their roles and responsibilities.

The health boards, renamed as health authorities, will be responsible for providing, directly or indirectly, all health and personal social services in their functional areas. The statutory definition of their role will take account of the increased emphasis in modern health care on health promotion and illness prevention.

The Department of Health will no longer be involved in the detailed management of the health services

There will be more effective accountability at all levels on the structure

Because of the need to have a body with comprehensive responsibility for all health and personal social services in the Eastern region, there will be a new health authority to replace the Eastern Health Board. In view of the size of the population to be served and the range and complexity of the services to be provided, the new authority will operate through a number of management areas within the region. The emphasis at area level will be to achieve the maximum integration of hospital and community services and to reflect local needs and priorities.

Functions of the boards of the health authorities

A new allocation of functions within all health authorities, between the boards and their management teams, will address criticisms about the confusion of policy functions and executive functions. Policy functions will be carried out directly by the boards while operational functions will be delegated to management. Of course, the Chief Executive Officer and his/her management team will have a key role in the development of policy, but the board's ultimate responsibility for the decisions will be unambiguous.

The legislation will specify that the following functions are reserved for the boards of the authorities:

- Deciding on a multi-annual strategic plan based on the identified needs of its population and taking account of statutory requirements and national policy guidelines.

- Determining, at the beginning of each year, the level of services to be provided within the expenditure limits set by the allocation.

- Agreeing and submitting to the Minister a budget for those services within the expenditure limits determined by the allocation.

The devolution of responsibility for the determination of regional priorities must be accompanied by more effective accountability at all levels in the structure. Measures will be taken to improve financial control in the health authorities and to make them more accountable for the services they provide. The Government is, during 1994, providing £100 million to meet the accumulated excess debts of the health boards and voluntary hospitals and to place them on a new financial footing. The financial controls which will be introduced are intended to reinforce budgetary observance and to ensure that such indebtedness will not arise again. Specific proposals include:

- The requirement on boards of the authorities to determine a budget within a fixed period and Ministerial sanctions which can be exercised when a board does not observe budgetary discipline.

- The requirement on boards to monitor the delivery of services, to take corrective action where necessary, and to be accountable to the Minister through new procedures.

- The publication by boards of a comprehensive annual report on activity and on the health status of their region.

Functions of the management of the health authorities

In addition to the development of policy, the Chief Executive Officer and his/her management team will be responsible for the management of services. While being fully accountable to the board, the management will have the autonomy necessary to perform its functions in an effective and efficient way.

The detailed management structure will be worked out at health authority level so that local conditions can be taken into account. For instance, the management structure appropriate to the Dublin area may not be appropriate elsewhere. A special emphasis will be placed on providing structures which encourage the development of linkages between services.

Some developments, which will improve the quality of management, will apply across the health authorities:

- Managers at all levels will have clearly defined responsibilities and will be fully accountable for achieving targets.

- The Department of Health will continue to work with the health authorities to introduce more efficient management practices.

- There will be a new emphasis on training and development of staff at all levels.

Role of the voluntary sector

The voluntary sector plays an integral role in the provision of health and personal social services in Ireland which is perhaps unparalleled in any other country. Traditionally, voluntary organisations have been to the forefront in identifying needs in the community and developing responses to them. Their independence enables them to harness community support and to complement the statutory services in an innovative and flexible manner.

Agencies in the voluntary sector range from major hospitals and national organisations to small community-based support groups set up in response to local needs. Some receive the bulk of their funding from the State, whether directly from the Department of Health or through the health boards; others receive some financial support to supplement the funds which they raise themselves.

The direct funding of some voluntary agencies by the Department of Health impedes the proper co-ordination and development of services at a local level. In particular it hampers the development of links between community and hospital services, and between statutory and voluntary services.

In future the voluntary agencies will receive funding from the health authorities, to whom they will be accountable for the public funds which they have received.

For the first time a specific statutory framework will be created between the health authorities and the voluntary agencies which recognises the role and responsibilities of both parties. The independent identity of the voluntary agencies will be fully respected under the new structure. They will retain their operational autonomy but will be fully accountable for the public funds which they receive. They will continue to have a direct input to the overall development of policy at national level.

The larger voluntary agencies will have service agreements with the health authorities which will link funding by the authorities to agreed levels of service to be provided by the agencies.

It is envisaged that these agreements will, in general, be for terms of a number of years. This will give voluntary agencies a greater guarantee of continuity than was possible in the past. These agreements will set general parameters in relation to the level of funding and the associated service requirement. The amount of funding which can be provided in any year cannot be guaranteed in advance; this will depend on the resources and service requirements given to the health authorities by the Department of Health. The agreements will therefore provide that the precise level of funding, and the associated service requirement, will be determined annually between the authorities and the agencies concerned.

The independent identity of voluntary agencies will be fully respected

It is recognised that formal agreements of this type would not be appropriate for the smaller voluntary groups who receive some financial assistance towards their activities. While it is important that they too are accountable for the public funds which they receive, the reporting procedure will be simplified and tailored to their circumstances.

Structures for public health

Structures for the planning and evaluation of health programmes and services will be an important element in implementing the Health Strategy. A Regional Public Health Department will therefore be established in each health board area to provide a co-ordinated and integrated approach to epidemiology and to support the planning and evaluation of services. It will have a key role in:

- Epidemiological research into conditions of ill-health and disease patterns in the region.

- The surveillance of communicable diseases, and the planning of targets, programmes and procedures for their prevention and control.

- The provision of advice regarding preventive medicine programmes.

- Participation in the adaptation of national targets and guidelines to provide appropriate indicators and evaluation mechanisms for use in assessing the effectiveness of programmes and services in the region.

- Participation, with other disciplines, in the monitoring and evaluation of the outcomes of health services.

Each Regional Department of Public Health will be headed by a Director of Public Health who will be a member of the health board's management team, reporting to the Chief Executive Officer, and will include public health specialists in its staffing. The Public Health Departments will have close functional, advisory and working relationships with those responsible for the implementation of programmes and services, and will ensure that the objectives which form the core of the Health Strategy will be constantly to the forefront in the decision-making process.

Performance measurement

One of the key roles of the Department of Health will be the evaluation of the service and financial performance of the regional authorities against national objectives. While the evaluation will embrace economy and efficiency, the focus will be concentrated increasingly on effectiveness, including the quality of services provided to patients and clients. Similarly, the boards and managements of the authorities will have to put in place more structured arrangements to measure the performance of their own units and of the agencies with which they have service agreements.

Initiatives which have already been taken in relation to the development of value-for-money structures and programmes, the promotion of medical audit, the development of data bases, the funding of acute hospitals by reference to their case-mix and the promulgation of a Patients Charter have together laid a good foundation for better measurement of performance.

The need to seek and demonstrate greater effectiveness in the delivery of public services is reflected in the provisions of the Comptroller and Auditor General (Amendment) Act, 1993. Bodies audited by the Comptroller and Auditor General will be subject, at his discretion, to examination by him regarding the economy and efficiency of their operations and the adequacy of the management systems which they have in place to appraise their own effectiveness.

As part of the restructuring of the Department of Health, which will follow from the devolution of some of its present work, arrangements will be made to support a structured annual performance review of health authorities. The Department will also support and encourage the development of suitable arrangements within health authorities to enable them to review the performance of their own cost centres and the agencies providing services on their behalf. Resources will be made available on a phased basis to promote the development of clinical audit and research focused on the effectiveness of current procedures and protocols across the various professions.

The emphasis in the review of performance will be to identify and diffuse good practice, to help agencies and professionals improve all aspects of performance in the planning and delivery of services, and to review policies and procedures in the light of the lessons learned from the review process. In a complex and costly service, such as health, one of the best guarantees of the good use of resources is a commitment to investigate how well the job is being done and to apply throughout the system the lessons learned from both good and poor practice. The development of a formal performance measurement function, supported by enhanced co-operation in the development and spread of good practice, is designed to achieve this.

Related services

While the Department of Social Welfare has responsibility for a wide range of income maintenance programmes, responsibility for the Disabled Person's Maintenance Allowance currently rests with the Department of Health. Similarly, both Departments have responsibilities in relation to dental, ophthalmic and aural services – the Department of Social Welfare operates the Treatment Benefits Scheme under the PRSI system while the Department of Health provides services for medical card holders and children through the health boards. In each of these areas, the scope for improving the service through changed organisational arrangements will be examined as an integral part of the implementation of the Health Strategy.

Equity and consistency in entitlements

The structure of eligibility for most of the major health services is clearly specified in legislation, which also governs the charges which can be made. For example, every Irish resident falls into one of two eligibility Categories:

- Those in Category One, known as medical card holders, who are entitled to a comprehensive range of health services free of charge.

- Those in Category Two, who are entitled to public hospital services subject to statutory charges, and who are also entitled to certain other services (mainly relating to assistance towards any excessive drugs costs). They are not entitled to free general practitioner services.

However, there are a number of services for which no eligibility criteria, or rules governing charges, are set down in legislation. In many cases, this is because the services have developed since the last major overhaul of the Health Act in 1970. These include services which now play a very important role in providing appropriate care in the community to people who might otherwise need residential care; for example, community paramedical services, home helps, meals on wheels and day care centres.

Because these services have developed in the absence of legislative guidelines, there are considerable differences from area to area in relation to the extent to which they are provided, who is entitled to receive them and what charges, if any, can be made. It is inequitable that a person's entitlement to a service should depend on the area in which he or she happens to live. National guidelines on eligibility and charges, which will be applied in a uniform manner in all areas, will be introduced in respect of all services where legislative provisions are at present absent. This development will form part of the reform of the basic framework of the health services and will be underpinned by the new legislation.

The new legislation will also update the existing provisions governing long-term care for those who are no longer able to look after themselves in the community. The Health (Nursing Homes) Act, 1990 has addressed the needs of those availing of private long-term care; those in public care are still governed by legislation which is now recognised as inadequate. The principle has always been accepted that people taken into long-term care should contribute from their incomes towards the cost of their maintenance; however, the legislation gives rise to anomalies and inequities as regards the charges which can be made and the basis upon which they can be made. The legislation will be amended to provide a clearer and fairer basis for these contributions towards the cost of long-term maintenance.

It is particularly important to ensure that the assessment procedures for medical card eligibility operate in an equitable manner, because of the very significant benefits available to medical card holders. Considerable progress has been made by the health boards in standardising their procedures and ensuring that they operate in the most consistent and uniform manner possible. Medical card eligibility procedures will continue to be reviewed, and whatever improvements are necessary in the interest of equity will be implemented.

A formal appeals system will be put in place in relation to medical cards, the Disabled Person's Maintenance Allowance and subventions towards private nursing home care.

The private sector

The mix of public and private service providers in the Irish healthcare system enables each to play a complementary role. The intent of the Health Strategy is not, therefore, to alter this mix in any radical fashion, but to enable the private sector to contribute to the achievement of the overall objectives.

The Government remains committed to maintaining the position of private practice, within the well established public/private mix. If, however, the market for private practice is to be sustained, it is essential that the current level of voluntary health insurance coverage is maintained, that there is a realistic acceptance by individual and institutional providers of what can be afforded, and that an appropriate balance is maintained between supply and demand in relation to available facilities. From July, 1994, it is probable that a competitive market will develop in health insurance in Ireland. While health insurers will be obliged to apply community rating, open enrolment and lifetime membership in their policies, the advent of competition may lead to a period of flux in existing patterns of supply and demand.

At present, the Minister for Health does not have any function in relation to the regulation, co-ordination or assessment of the services provided by **private hospitals**, other than in relation to maternity and psychiatric services. However, this sector fulfils an important function in meeting the overall health needs of the population. It provides about half of all the private accommodation available in the State and it is heavily reliant for funding on the Voluntary Health Insurance Board, which is in turn supported by tax relief on its premia. The sector draws most of its consultant medical manpower from the public hospital sector and relies on the public sector for the production of professionally qualified staff. There is, therefore, a considerable degree of interdependence between the public and the private sectors in the provision of hospital services for the population.

It is considered, having regard to the factors outlined above, that appropriate monitoring and consultative mechanisms should be established involving the Department of Health, the public health services and the institutional providers of private care. These mechanisms would enable the following matters to be addressed:

- The exchange of information on policy developments likely to affect the providers of private care.

- Ongoing review of the balance between supply and demand in the provision of facilities for private patients.

- The development of protocols, which would guide both the public and private systems on the further enhancement of technological capacity.

- Examining the processes in place in private hospitals for the maintenance of acceptable standards and good practice and the review of complaints made by or on behalf of patients.

The need for some form of regulation of the private sector can be considered in the light of the experience gained through the proposed consultative mechanisms.

Successive Governments have encouraged the provision of a mix of public and private practice in **public hospitals**. The Commission on Health Funding examined this policy and concluded that it facilitates the provision of a high quality public hospital service, particularly due to the retention of consultants of the highest calibre in the public system. However, it is important to ensure that the co-existence of public and private practice does not undermine the principle of equitable access. The discussion of acute hospital services in the Four-Year Action Plan details the continued steps which will be taken to ensure this.

General practitioners operate in the private sector in respect of 65 per cent of their patients. However, the services which they provide to their private patients have subsequent implications for other public services, particularly those in acute hospitals. While it is intended to retain the public/private mix, the measures which are being taken to develop the role of general practice and to integrate it better with other health services will have an impact on both its public and private components.

The health and personal
social services are first
and foremost about
people.

The health and personal social services are, first and foremost, about people — the patients and clients who receive the services, and the professional, administrative and support staff who provide them. The Health Strategy places a new emphasis on the importance of both of these sets of participants.

User satisfaction and participation

Serving the patient or client

The health and personal social services exist to serve the patient or client — this has not been sufficiently emphasised in the past. The services must therefore be consumer-oriented. It is accepted that there is much-room for improvement in that respect.

Chapter four

The **Participants**

Service quality

The Charter of Rights for Hospital Patients has been a first step in setting out clearly the reorientation of one major service towards a greater consumer-responsiveness. Further Charters will be introduced to cover groups such as children, expectant mothers, the elderly, the mentally ill and people with a physical or mental handicap. The adherence of the services to the principles set out in such Charters is an important indicator of one aspect of service quality. The technical quality of service, in terms of its outcome and effectiveness, can be evaluated by clinical audit mechanisms and, as discussed in chapter two, these can and should take the patient's perception into account. The measurement of patient satisfaction with more general aspects of the services, such as waiting-times or the manner in which services are delivered, can also be measured in various ways, such as consumer surveys. Health authorities will be required to carry out such evaluations and to include their findings in the annual reports which they will be making to the Minister. In addition, each health authority will be encouraged to identify and develop a "quality initiative" geared towards improving an aspect of service quality — such as, for example, an improved method of organising out-patient clinics. The initiatives which prove successful can then be adopted by the other authorities.

Information when needed

A second important method of increasing the consumer-orientation of the services is to ensure that detailed and accurate information is available when required. The Minister for Health has recently published a comprehensive Information Guide to our Health Services which has been widely circulated. In addition, very detailed information has been made available to Citizens' Information Centres and to other interested parties on eligibility guidelines and assessment procedures. The Department of Health and the health authorities will continue to ensure that patients and clients have ready access to the fullest possible information about their entitlements and how to avail of them.

A third strand in the consumer-orientation of the Health Strategy will be contained in the legislation to reform the framework of the services, as discussed in the previous chapter. This will include a number of measures to give individuals a better opportunity of having grievances redressed and to represent the views of users, as a group, in the decision-making process. Among these measures will be:

- The establishment of advisory groups in each health authority area to provide an input to the authority from the users of the various services.

- A requirement on all health authorities to put appropriate complaints procedures in place.

- The introduction of a statutory function of the boards of the health authorities to act as a channel to the Minister of the views and concerns of their populations.

Human resources

Services will stand or fall on the contribution of the staff who provide them. This country has been very fortunate in the quality and commitment of the more than 60,000 people working in the health and personal social services. The Health Strategy must focus on how they can be further encouraged and supported. The clear statements of the objectives and direction of the services, which are contained in the Strategy itself, will help this process; however, it is also important to improve training and other aspects of our human resources policies.

Planning our future manpower requirements

In addition to ensuring that people with the necessary expertise are available to the services, a suitable balance must be achieved between the demand for and supply of the many skills needed in a modern health system. Because so many of the skills required are highly specialised and mobile, it is recognised that manpower planning at the micro level poses difficulties. In specialist areas, the number of people in training and the number of vacancies arising in any one year are often small; the period of time spent in training can be relatively long, so that calculations of need at the beginning of a training cycle are often overtaken by events; many of the skills are in demand internationally and emigration of skilled personnel can upset calculations of predicted supply. Notwithstanding these difficulties, there is a need to keep the balance between supply and demand under review and a number of important issues require urgent attention.

Training of doctors There is a number of problems affecting medical manpower. The existing ratio of non-consultant hospital doctors to consultants is 2:1. One of the consequences of this distribution is the provision of a substantial proportion of hospital medical care by doctors in training. In addition, it is accepted that a more structured approach to postgraduate training is necessary. These issues are under active consideration by the Department of Health in consultation with various statutory bodies such as the Medical Council, Comhairle na nOspideal and the Postgraduate Medical and Dental Board, and appropriate policies will be developed.

Between 320 and 350 Irish doctors graduate from our medical schools each year. Even with the present manpower distribution, the medical schools are producing more Irish doctors than are likely to find career opportunities in Ireland. This is also an issue which will need consideration, in conjunction with the Department of Education.

General practitioners With the increasingly important role of the general practitioner in the provision of health services, it is necessary to ensure that the number of doctors in general practice is appropriate to meet the needs of the population effectively. A comprehensive review will be carried out of the manpower

Services will stand or fall on the contribution of the staff who provide them

This strategy has implications for the way in which the professional groups are trained and educated

requirements of general practice as a whole and the requirements for the GMS scheme.

Nurse training The major overhaul of nurse training which is referred to later will have implications for the number of nurses in training. Such numbers will have to be adapted to the requirements of the new training regime.

Other professions The development of services and the trend towards specialisation has created a demand for a wide range of skills in many of the other professions in the health and personal social services. The output of many of these from the education/training system has not kept pace with demand. This has led to shortages in key areas. These will be examined in co-operation with the education authorities and professional bodies concerned with a view to increasing the numbers in training.

Developing our managers

The growing complexity of the health and personal social services reinforces the need to strengthen the management capacity throughout the system. The current recruitment procedures and management development and training programmes will be urgently reviewed to produce a strategy for developing the required management capacity over the next decade. The strategy will be devised in consultation with the CEOs of the health boards, hospital managements, the relevant educational and training bodies and staff interests and will be operational as soon as possible.

In addition to strengthening general management, specific initiatives are necessary in relation to the involvement of the medical, nursing and other professions in management. In accordance with the revised common contract, consultants are now expected to manage their own practices through the development of practice plans. Pilot studies on consultant involvement in management are underway in St James's Hospital, Dublin, Cork Regional Hospital, Wexford General Hospital and in the Hospital Programme of the North Western Health Board. In addition, the Department of Health will continue its active support of the Diploma course in Clinical Management developed by the Royal College of Surgeons in Ireland and the Institute of Public Administration. The future training and educational programmes for nurses and other professionals will emphasise the contribution which they can and should make to the efficient running of the healthcare system.

Training and education

The reorientation of the health delivery system set out in this Strategy will necessitate a detailed examination of its implications for the way in which the professional groups who deliver the services are trained and educated. Some consideration has already been given to this issue, but this will now be accelerated and completed in a structured manner.

Because of the rapidly-changing nature of health services, all staff need to be aware of the need for continuing education and training. The exact provisions made for postgraduate training and continuing training in each staff category will be examined and developed where required.

Consultations will take place immediately with all the bodies responsible for the training and education of professionals in the health sector so that whatever changes are necessary will be made in their programmes to ensure the appropriate range of skills and expertise.

Irish nursing enjoys a well-deserved international reputation for excellence. However, to preserve this status, it is now necessary to align the regime for nursing education more closely with the demands of the modern day health service. This is a corollary to the rapid pace of service development in recent years, with an added emphasis being placed on primary care, and the growing need for new knowledge and skills to cope with the role of nursing in the 1990s.

The changes to be introduced will be informed by the views of the profession. In broad terms, the proposed changes will include:

- Pre-registration training programmes provided by nurse training schools with an active input from third level colleges of education.

- Allocating more time to community placements.

- Gaining formal accreditation of all relevant educational and training achievements.

- Making explicit investment in continuing education for nurses within a formal structure.

This process of change will start during 1994, in consultation with An Bord Altranais and relevant staff interests, and the reforms will be implemented as speedily as possible. They will constitute the single most significant investment in nursing education in recent decades.

Our objective is to give a
clear sense of direction to
the health services.

The development of the Health Strategy does not end with the publication of **_Shaping a healthier future_**; rather, it is a stage in what will be an ongoing process. This chapter explains the document's role in that process, and then outlines the further stages.

Chapter five

The **Next Steps**

The role of this document

The principal purpose of *Shaping a healthier future* is to give a clear sense of direction to the health services, in terms of the underlying principles and the proposed reorientation in the way that services are planned and delivered.

Each of the three preceding chapters addressed one of the three dimensions of the necessary reorientation, i.e.

- **The services** — focusing the services on improvements in health status and the quality of life, and increasing the emphasis on the provision of the most appropriate care.

- **The framework** — providing for more decision-making and accountability at regional level, allied to better methods of performance measurement.

- **The participants** — placing a greater emphasis on the importance of the patients and clients who receive the services and the staff who provide them.

The three key principles, defined in the first chapter, are also seen to underpin the overall Strategy:

- The achievement of greater equity will be helped by measures such as targeting of programmes towards "health development sectors", improving services so as to meet unaddressed needs or reduce waiting-times, and ensuring consistency in determining entitlements and charging arrangements.

- The emphasis on quality of service will be reinforced through the development of clinical audit programmes, charters for various client-groups and the requirement on health authorities to include formal evaluations of patient satisfaction levels as part of their annual performance report to the Minister.

- The various strands of the principle of accountability run throughout the Strategy — the organisational and management reforms will improve legal and financial accountability, the development of clinical audit programmes will emphasise the accountability of healthcare professionals, while the measures to increase consumer-responsiveness will address the need for accountability on the part of those who plan and deliver services to those who receive them.

Further documents

The next stage of the process will include the publication of a number of further documents which will deal in greater detail with aspects of the implementation of the Strategy. These will include:

- A detailed Health Promotion Strategy, which will develop the discussion of health promotion in this document and which will set out more detailed goals and targets and plans for their achievement.

- A national policy on alcohol.

- A White Paper on Mental Health

- A discussion document on Women's Health.

- A policy document on Travellers' Health.

- The report of the Review Group on Health Services for Persons with a Physical or Sensory Disability.

In addition, legislation will be published to provide for the improved accountability and the reorganisation of the framework of the system as discussed in detail in chapter three.

The implementation of the Strategy

The sense of direction provided by the Strategy is intended to inform decision-making at all levels of the health services — from the process of determining policy at national and at regional level to the approach taken by health professionals and other staff in the delivery of individual services.

Detailed plans and targets will now be developed on foot of the Strategy. The accompanying Four-Year Action Plan sets out national targets for reductions in risk factors associated with premature mortality, and for improvements in other indicators of health status, along with details of how these can be achieved, and also sets out national objectives for service development on the basis of the directions and principles of the Strategy. These must now be translated into more detailed targets and programmes at national and at regional level and, where appropriate, beyond.

> **Principles must now be translated into more detailed targets and programmes at national and at regional level**

A process of consultation This implementation is of concern to all the various participants in the health and personal social services — the health boards, other agencies, staff and consumer interests. The development of health policy over the years has benefited greatly from the consultative process, both formal and informal. In preparing this Strategy, account has been taken of the submissions made in the formal consultative processes which were instigated following the report of the Commission on Health Funding in 1989, and the 1991 announcement of the Government's general intentions for organisational reform in the health services.

It is very clear that the issues raised in the Strategy, and the action planned to implement it, will have wide-ranging consequences both for those who receive services and for those who deliver them. It is essential therefore that the message of the Strategy is disseminated as widely as possible so that everybody is aware of what precisely it means, what effects it will have and the detail of what will happen. To achieve this, a comprehensive Communications Programme has been drawn up which is designed to explain the Strategy at national level and at local level. Each health board has designated a Health Strategy Co-ordinator to take responsibility for this programme and to act as a liaison contact during the implementation process.

The Minister for Health now invites all interested parties to consider the policy directions set out in this document. He would welcome, and will encourage in every way possible, national debate about the implications of the Strategy and about how it may best be implemented. The views which emerge will be taken into account in the detailed implementation of the Strategy, both at national level and within the health board areas.

Ongoing review The implementation of the Strategy will be subject to ongoing monitoring and review through, in particular, the introduction of the system of annual reports for each region which will encompass health status, service provision and measures of patient satisfaction, and the structured annual performance review which will be the responsibility of the Department of Health.

The many strengths of our health system were outlined at the start of this document; it also identified the weaknesses which have prevented the services from delivering on their full potential. With the new sense of direction embodied in this Strategy, we can work together to remove these obstacles and to develop a service of the highest quality and effectiveness.

A Four-Year Action Plan translates this Strategy into specific targets for action.

The following pages set out the Four-Year Action Plan for the implementation of the Health Strategy over the period 1994-1997. It includes:

- National targets for reductions in risk factors associated with premature mortality, and for improvements in other indicators of health status. The dates for achievement of some of the targets go beyond 1997; however, the Action Plan describes what must be done over the next four years to be on course to achieve them.

The **Four-Year Action Plan** 1994 - 1997

- National objectives for service development on the basis of the directions and principles of the Strategy.

As explained in chapter five of the Strategy, these must be translated into more detailed targets and objectives at national and regional level and, where appropriate, beyond, and this process will take account of the views of all interested parties.

The term health boards is used throughout the Action Plan to refer both to the present health boards and to the health authorities which will result from the legislation discussed in chapter three.

Health promotion

A central aspect of the Strategy is to reorient the health services towards a health promotion approach based on encouraging people to take responsibility for their own health and on providing the environmental support necessary to achieve this. Many of the targets in this Strategy depend crucially on a co-ordinated and integrated approach to health promotion. The Department of Health will publish a comprehensive strategy on health promotion. It will review progress so far and set out in more detail than in this Strategy the initiatives proposed for the future.

Target

To develop health promotion programmes in school, community, workplace and health service settings so as to promote health at local level.

To be achieved by:

- Information and education programmes, including those on skills relating to making healthy choices in lifestyle.

- Increasing the awareness of health professionals such as general practitioners and public health nurses of the need to encourage a health-promotion approach.

- Use of multi-media campaigns.

The Department of Health through the Health Promotion Unit will continue to liaise with the Department of Education on the development and dissemination of suitable materials for inclusion in social and health education programmes in schools, such as those currently available in the North-Western and Mid-Western Health Boards.

Priority targets

Chapter two of the Strategy identified cancer, cardiovascular disease and accidents as the three main causes of premature mortality in Ireland. It set a medium-term target for addressing each of them and listed six areas in which risk reduction targets and action programmes would be focused. These were:

- Smoking

- Alcohol

- Nutrition and diet

- Cholesterol and blood pressure

- Exercise

- Causes of accidents

These areas are now considered in detail.

Smoking

Target

To reduce the percentage of those who smoke by at least 1 percentage point per year so that more than 80 per cent of the population aged fifteen years and over are non-smokers by the year 2000.

To be achieved by:

- Extending the environmental controls over tobacco, especially those in the workplace.

- Reducing the allowable budgets for advertising of tobacco products and sponsorship by tobacco manufacturers and distributors by five per cent per annum.

- Continuing and intensifying multi-media anti-tobacco campaigns and health education programmes.

- Government fiscal policies which take account of the need to discourage smoking.

- Continued action by doctors and other health professionals to encourage a decrease in smoking.

Alcohol

Baseline data for monitoring progress in achieving the targets below will be established during 1994. The targets themselves will be reviewed when the baseline data become available.

Target

To promote moderation in the consumption of alcohol and to reduce the risks to physical, mental and family health that can arise from alcohol misuse.

To be achieved by:

- A national policy on alcohol which will be adopted and launched during the next twelve months.

 1 small glass of spirits
= **1 unit**

 1 glass of wine
= **1 unit**

 ½ pint of beer
= **1 unit**

Target

To ensure that, within the next four years, 75 per cent of the population aged fifteen years and over knows and understands the recommended sensible limits for alcohol consumption. While these limits are subject to ongoing research, the present international consensus is 14 units per week for a woman and 21 units for a man.

To be achieved by:

- A series of information/ education campaigns and programmes which will raise people's awareness about sensible drinking practices. Health professionals will have a key role in this regard.

Target

To reduce substantially over the next ten years the proportion of those who exceed the recommended sensible limits for alcohol consumption.

To be achieved by:

- Implementation of the national policy on alcohol which will be launched during the next twelve months.

These targets will be of particular importance in the context of road accidents, where alcohol features so significantly in premature death.

IT IS OUR POLICY TO ENCOURAGE A SMOKE FREE ENVIRONMENT IN OUR OFFICES

Nutrition and diet

Target

To encourage changes in the Irish diet by the year 2000 so as to include the recommended amount of essential nutrients and to provide the right levels of energy. The need for a reduction in fat consumption and an increased fibre intake in the population will also be addressed. (Targets for these areas are discussed in more detail in the *Nutrition Health Promotion — Framework for Action* published by the Health Promotion Unit of the Department of Health).

To be achieved by:

- Developing a long-term food and nutrition policy and, in the meantime, implementing the five-year framework for action on nutrition which was developed by the Department of Health in 1991. The framework includes a series of healthy eating guide-lines which will continue to be promoted.

- Maintaining a national nutrition surveillance system.

- Building, in co-operation with the Department of Education, on the Health Promotion Unit's programme on nutrition in schools which was piloted in the Eastern and North-Western Health Board areas.

- Extending to other areas the community-based initiative on nutrition for lower socio-economic groups which operates at present in the Eastern Health Board area.

- Continuing the present steps to promote good nutrition such as the annual National Healthy Eating Week. The Health Promotion Unit will continue to publish leaflets on nutrition and healthy eating.

- Introducing an information programme on the dangers of obesity.

- Involving doctors and other health professionals in promoting changes in diet.

Cholesterol and blood pressure

Programmes for the prevention of heart disease and strokes are based on population and high risk individual strategies, and include relevant risk reduction measures in each case. Appropriate targets for cholesterol and blood pressure have been the subject of medical debate, and this will be examined in detail in the health promotion strategy to be published later this year. The two conditions are, of course, influenced by smoking, alcohol consumption, diet and exercise and the action proposed in each of these areas will have a positive impact on both.

Exercise

These targets are also subject to review in the light of baseline data which will be acquired in 1994.

Targets

- **To achieve a 30 per cent increase in the proportion of the population aged 15 and over who engage in an accumulated thirty minutes of light physical exercise most days of the week by the year 2000.**

- **To achieve a 20 per cent increase in the proportion of the population aged 15 and over who engage in moderate exercise for at least twenty minutes, three times a week, by the year 2000.**

To be achieved by:

- Joint action by the Departments of Health, Education and the Environment in conjunction with community and statutory groups (such as Cospóir) to encourage participation in sports and to promote the value of regular exercise.

- The continuation of the *Be Active Be Alive* programme and information programmes generally.

Causes of accidents

A wide range of agencies have an impact on accident prevention and a multi-sectoral approach is therefore needed. Much of the action necessary to prevent accidents is focused in agencies outside the health services. In particular, the National Safety Council has a statutory responsibility for the promotion of road and water safety and fire prevention. The Council arranges education, training programmes and publicity campaigns. The National Authority for Occupational Safety and Health is responsible for ensuring an effective system of enforcing standards for health and safety at work, promoting actions to improve health and safety at work and providing information and advice relating to the prevention of accidents and ill-health at work.

The implications of accidents for the healthcare system are significant. They involve the provision of:

- Effective ambulance services.

- Hospital accident and emergency services.

- Highly intensive hospital in-patient services.

- Rehabilitation services.

- Long-term care and income maintenance allowances for those disabled by accidents.

Given the multi-sectoral approach and concerted action required to achieve a reduction in accidents, the Minister for Health will liaise with the Ministers having responsibility for the relevant agencies so as to agree appropriate mechanisms for co-operation and co-ordination in their accident reduction initiatives.

General practitioner services

The general practitioner service will be better organised and supported in fulfilling a wider and more integrated role in the healthcare system.

General practitioners, whether in family practice, in occupational health, as medical officers to homes or institutions, or in organised screening or preventive activities, are a key ingredient of primary healthcare. Ireland has been very fortunate in the quality and commitment of those working in general practice.

In the mid 1980s a Working Party carried out an examination of the General Medical Services and identified the factors which contribute towards the provision of a good quality general practitioner service. These were:

- Ready and immediate access by patients to doctors regardless of means.

- A close personal relationship between the general practitioner and an identifiable and reasonably constant group of patients and families.

- A holistic approach to the care of patients, taking full account of the psychological, social and environmental factors influencing patients' health status.

- A concern with prevention and anticipatory care as well as effective response to illness.

- An ability to reach fully rounded diagnoses, often under pressure, on the basis of special training for conditions met in general practice.

Significant progress has been made in developing the services along these lines in recent years and it is the intention that this will continue in the forthcoming GMS review. However, if it is to fulfil its functions adequately, the general practitioner service must be better organised and better integrated with other health services to enable it to function as an integral part of the work of the healthcare system in patient care. Better management structures must also be developed to support the delivery of quality care by general practitioners for all their patients.

In more specific terms, the following organisational and service problems must be tackled:

- The fragmentation of general practice and the isolation of general practitioners. Approximately 59 per cent of general practitioners operate from single handed practices. Only 15 per cent operate from practices with three or more doctors. This makes it both difficult and costly to fund desirable developments. General practitioners often work in isolation from other general practitioners, community care services and hospitals. The manner in which general practice is currently organised leads to inefficiencies in the use of resources, duplication of costs and increased workload for doctors. The inevitable result is an inadequately supported and equipped structure incapable of providing appropriate services in a cost effective manner.

- The lack of epidemiological data relating to disease process and morbidity in the community.

- The lack of a defined practice population. Since there is no definite list of private patients, the GP in many cases does not know what his or her total practice population is in terms of either numbers or named patients. In the past, research in Dublin has shown that approximately 11 per cent of families with young children reported not having a general practitioner. A similar percentage attending at Accident and Emergency Departments in Dublin hospitals recently reported having no general practitioner. In the Dublin setting at least, the general practice population is not stable:

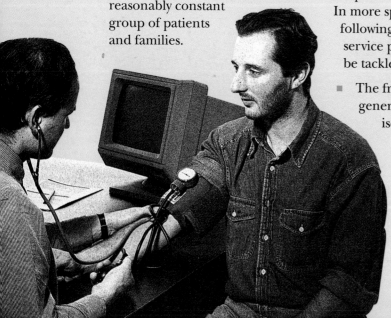

■ A proportion of patients do not closely identify with one general practitioner. They freely change from doctor to doctor and practice to practice.

■ In a proportion of families, different members attend different doctors and practices.

The following steps will be taken over the next four years to develop general practice and to help it fulfil a wider integrated role.

■ Incentives for the improved organisation of general practice will be designed so that patients have easier access to a wider range of services provided by their family doctor. Assistance will be targeted on group practices, amalgamated practices or co-operative type arrangements.

■ A number of single-centre or multi-centre group practices will be established on a pilot basis. These will provide a comprehensive range of primary healthcare services and will have close links with the hospital services.

■ The general practice units which have been established in each health board will make arrangements with individual practices to provide additional services where this would be done more cost-effectively than at present.

■ The new Departments of Public Health Medicine in each health board will liaise closely with general practitioners on exchanging epidemiological data. The aim is to have 80 per cent of GMS practices computerised within four years so as to improve the sharing of information and help practice management.

■ The general practice units will seek to introduce a system of patient registration. This will help to expand the general practitioner's role into areas such as preventive medicine, including vaccination programmes.

■ The development of a detailed information network for general practitioners, including the establishment of a national drugs information unit, so as to promote better quality and more cost effective prescribing. The result will be improved drug therapy for patients and the freeing up of resources to enable general practitioners to develop their practice by, for example, the purchase of more equipment or through improvements in their surgeries.

■ The Irish College of General Practitioners will be supported in the development of quality assurance measures for general practice.

■ Vocational and post-graduate education of doctors will be supported and co-ordinated so as to maintain the highest possible standards among general practitioners.

A range of other measures will be introduced to improve the linkages between general practice and the other health services, particularly the acute general hospitals. These will include:

■ Improving co-operation between hospitals and general practitioners in each major hospital catchment area by:

■ Involving general practitioners in activities which are currently undertaken by hospitals but are more appropriate to the community setting.

■ Developing protocols of combined care for specific conditions between consultants and general practitioners.

■ Giving general practitioners access to appropriate investigative facilities and other services within hospitals.

■ Involving general practitioners in the care of specific groups. Among the steps that will continue to be promoted are:

■ A domiciliary care programme for people who are terminally ill.

■ Involving general practitioners in a screening programme for children whose health status may be vulnerable.

■ Using the general practice units to make arrangements with general practitioners for caring for elderly people at home where they would otherwise have to go to hospital.

Dental services

The deficiencies in the public dental service will be tackled over the next four years in the context of an integrated dental development plan which will also involve the phased extension of eligibility to children under 16 years. There will be continued steps to achieve further progress in oral health targets.

The key aims of the public dental service are to:

- Reduce the level of dental disease in children.

- Improve the level of oral health in the population overall.

- Provide adequate treatment services to children and to all medical card holders. Until now, the eligibility of children for the public dental service has been confined to those in pre-school and primary school age-groups.

Significant progress has been made in achieving these aims and many of the oral health goals which were set in 1984 and to be achieved in the year 2000 have already been achieved. For instance the target of 80% of 5 year olds, in optimally fluoridated areas, to be free of dental caries was achieved in 1992 and the target of an average number of 27 natural teeth in the 16 to 24 age group was achieved in 1990.

Despite the achievements made to date there are deficiencies in our treatment services and significant further progress can be made in improving the overall oral health status of the population. An integrated plan will therefore be implemented over the next 4 years which will involve:

- Increased efficiency of water fluoridation schemes, continuous upgrading of existing water fluoridation plants and appropriate increases in the numbers of water fluoridation plants.

- Wider use of fluorides in general and especially in the less than optimally fluoridated areas by such means as school-based fluoride-rinsing schemes and by more frequent and regular use of fluoride toothpaste.

- Oral health education programmes aimed at the family, at population groups and at individuals through the media and in healthcare and educational settings.

- The phased extension of eligibility for public dental services to children under 16 years, beginning with an extension to those under 14 years in 1994.

- The phased improvement of primary and secondary orthodontic care for all children.

- The expansion of hospital oral surgery services to provide adequately for those who require specialised treatment.

- The phased introduction of new arrangements for the provision of dental care to eligible adults.

- Improvements in the school dental services to ensure the systematic screening of children in 3 designated classes in primary and post primary schools.

- The establishment of a standardised database in each health board for monitoring changes in oral health.

The aims of this plan will be to achieve the following oral health goals by the year 2000:

- At least 85 per cent of five-year-olds in optimally fluoridated areas and at least 60 per cent of five-year-olds in less than optimally fluoridated areas will be free of dental caries (baby teeth only).

- Twelve-year-old children will have on average no more than 1 decayed, missing or filled permanent tooth in optimally fluoridated areas and on average no more than 2 decayed, missing or filled permanent teeth in less than optimally fluoridated areas.

- The average number of natural teeth present in 16-24 year olds will be 27.7. This compares with a current average of 27.2 and represents an average gain of one tooth for every two people in that age category.

- No more than 2 per cent of 35-to-44-year-olds will have no natural teeth.

- No more than 42 per cent of people aged 65 years and over will have no natural teeth.

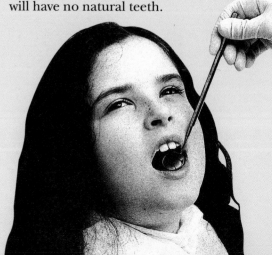

Women's health

The Government will publish a plan for women's health that will be implemented over the next four years.

At present, health services for women are organised by function. There are separate maternity and gynaecology services, family planning services, mammography, cervical screening and welfare services. There is no framework that provides unified objectives or common approaches. What is required is a policy that is based on a comprehensive view of women and the issues that affect their health.

To this end the Department of Health is preparing a discussion document on women's health which takes account of the recommendations of the *Second Commission on the Status of Women.* This discussion document will be published in 1994 and comments will be invited on it. The Government's plan for women's health will then be put in place.

In advance of the plan some major elements underlying government policy on women's health services are set out below. The objectives will include the following:

■ To ensure that women's health needs are identified and planned for in a comprehensive way.

■ To ensure that women receive the health and welfare services that they need at the right time and in a way that respects their dignity and individuality. They must have ease of access to and continuity of care.

■ To promote greater consultation with women about their health and welfare needs. This must be done at national, regional and local level.

■ To promote within the health services a greater participation by women both in the more senior positions and at the representative levels.

The priorities for developing women's health services, subject to what emerges from consultations with interested groups on the discussion document, will be:

■ To make maternity services more responsive to the needs of mothers who now seek more individual care and a greater involvement in decision-making about their care.

■ To expand the services for women who are victims of rape and domestic violence, and to co-ordinate these services more effectively with other health services.

Family planning services are discussed in a separate section.

A further aspect to women's health is the provision of appropriate preventive services such as cervical screening and screening for breast cancer. These are discussed below.

Some 70 women die each year from cervical cancer, most of whom have never been screened.

The purpose of a cervical smear is to detect the presence of pre-cancerous lesions which can easily be cured. Once the disease reaches the cancerous stage there is no known cure. From the information currently available the percentage of abnormal smears is highest in the 25-34 age group at about 36 per cent. Because, however, of the lengthy incubation period for the disease, deaths from cervical cancer occur in the older age groups.

All aspects of the cervical screening service are currently being reviewed by an expert group which is due to report within the coming months. The Minister proposes to reorganise the service taking account of the group's recommendations.

In relation to screening for breast cancer, a decision will be taken on the question of setting up a national screening service as soon as the findings of the present study at the Mater Hospital Foundation have been evaluated.

Health boards will be required to make special arrangements for the care of traveller women. These are discussed in a later section.

Family planning

An accessible and comprehensive family planning service will be developed in each health board area on a phased basis by the end of 1995.

The comprehensive family planning service will include:

- Education, counselling and advice on all legal methods of contraception.

- Ready access to these methods, including:

  - Natural methods of family planning.

  - Medical contraceptives, such as the pill and spermicides.

  - Non-medical contraceptives, such as condoms, IUDs and diaphragms.

  - Male and female sterilisation services i.e. vasectomies and tubal ligations.

- Advice, counselling and the provision of certain services in relation to infertility.

General practitioners provide a wide range of family planning services and will continue to play a central role in this area. However, if the service needs to be complemented, for example in the interest of patient choice, it is envisaged that this would be achieved by the establishment and maintenance, either by the health boards or by other bodies acting on their behalf, of designated family planning clinics in major urban areas.

Each health board will immediately begin an evaluation of the current family planning needs and services in its area, and determine the services which it will have to provide or have provided on its behalf in order to have an accessible and comprehensive family planning service in place by the end of 1995.

The sections dealing with individual groups such as travellers and drug misusers deal with their needs in relation to family planning and safer sex practices.

Children's health

There will be a detailed review of the pre-school and child health services during 1994. There will also be improvements in other services taking account of the existing reports on maternity and infant care and on immunisation.

The priority given to preventive care for children is a key factor in determining their subsequent health status. The main issues to be considered are the best means of monitoring the progress of young children and identifying health problems as early as possible; the best approaches to immunisation; and, for babies, the promotion of breast feeding.

The last review of Child Health Services took place in 1967. Recommendations as to the most appropriate pre-school and school health services were made on the basis of knowledge and medical practice current at that time. Changes in the health status of children, demographic changes, and the far-reaching developments and improvements in Child Health Services involving the primary and secondary health sectors indicate that alterations may be required in the way certain of these services are organised and delivered.

Certain elements of the overall services for children, such as the Maternity and Infant Care Scheme and the Immunisation Services have already been the subject of recent reviews and the recommendations made by these reviews are included in the sections which follow. A fundamental review of the other elements of Child Health Services such as pre-school and school services will be carried out in 1994. The aim will be to implement recommendations as to the most effective service in tune with modern thinking and practice in child health.

Infant care

Services delivered in the post-natal period and in the first year of life are a critical component of infant care and child health.

The recommendations on infant care of the Review Group on Maternity and Infant Care will be implemented as follows:

- Every baby will have a visit from the Public Health Nurse as soon as possible after discharge from the maternity hospital/unit, ideally during the first 24 hours.

- Every baby will have two designated visits to the general practitioner, one at two weeks and the other at six weeks after birth.

- Liaison arrangements between the general practitioner and the Public Health Nurse will be strengthened to ensure continuing care as required.

Immunisation programmes

The National Immunisation Programme will be rationalised in accordance with the recommendations of the Review Group on Immunisation dealing with the objectives of:

- Eliminating communicable diseases such as pertussis, measles, mumps, rubella, poliomyelitis and Hib-related disease by:

  - Achieving and maintaining a minimum of 95 per cent uptake of the National Immunisation Programme in each Community Care Area.

  - Introducing mechanisms to ensure that each child has completed the programme of immunisation appropriate to him/her, in accordance with the National Schedule of Immunisation, by the age of 15 months for DPT/Polio/Hib and 24 months for MMR.

The rationalisation of the National Immunisation Programme will be achieved through:

- Improving the notification and call/recall systems to ensure that parents have their children immunised by the due dates.

- Promoting the benefits of immunisation to the public and to health professionals.

- Targeting parents in areas where the uptake of immunisation is low and/or levels of communicable diseases are high.

- Improving co-ordination between maternity hospitals/ units, vaccinating doctors and parents.

- Improving co-operation between National Schools and the health boards to ensure children entering school are immunised fully.

- Involving general practitioners to a greater extent in the immunisation programme.

Pending the completion of the review of the other child health services each health board shall ensure that the current pre-school services are maintained.

Health centres

Health centres play a crucial role in the provision of preventive and other services in the community, particularly in relation to children's health. More health centres will be provided and priority will also be given to the improvement of existing centres where necessary.

Child care and family support services

Breast feeding

Targets

To increase the use of breast feeding so that:

- The initiation rate (i.e. the proportion of all new born babies who are breast fed at first) will have risen to 35 per cent by 1996 and 50 per cent by the year 2000 against a base figure of 32 per cent in 1990.

- By 2000 30 per cent of all babies will still be breast fed at the age of four months. This compares with a base rate of about 12 per cent in 1990.

To be achieved by:

- Action consequent upon the recommendations of the National Committee to Promote Breast Feeding.

Support services for children at risk and families in difficulty will be strengthened in co-operation with relevant voluntary bodies in accordance with the principles enshrined in the Child Care Act.

Many changes have taken place in Irish society in recent years. Generally speaking these have brought considerable benefits to us as individuals and as a community. However we have also seen the growth of social problems affecting children and their parents such as family breakdown, child abuse and neglect and youth homelessness. The health and personal social services have played and continue to play a key role in providing both services and supports for children and families who find themselves in such difficulties.

At any one time almost 3,000 children are in the care of the health boards, most because their parents are under stress and unable to cope but some due to child abuse and neglect. In 1986 the number of reports of alleged abuse received by health boards was just over 1000. In almost 500 of these cases the abuse was confirmed including 274 cases of child sexual abuse. The latest figures available indicate that health boards are now receiving almost 4000 reports of alleged abuse each year, of which about 1500 cases are confirmed including about 600 cases of sexual abuse.

The Child Care Act 1991 was enacted against this background. It imposes a clear statutory duty on the health boards to provide a range of child care and family support services to assist parents in caring for their children and to avoid, as far as possible, the need to place children in care. In addition the Act:

- Improves the procedures for intervention by health boards, the Gardaí and the Courts where children are at risk.

- Requires health boards to provide accommodation for homeless young people.

- Introduces a system for the inspection and supervision of pre-school services.

- Provides for the registration and inspection of children's residential centres.

All sections of the Child Care Act will be implemented by the end of 1996. Priority will be given to those provisions which confer new and improved powers on health boards, the Gardaí and the Courts to intervene more effectively in cases of child abuse and neglect.

A major programme of investment in the child care services has been drawn up to ensure that the Act is fully and properly implemented.

During 1993 a range of new service developments, costing £10m in a full year, were approved including:

- Over 100 new posts of social worker and child care worker.

- Three new consultant-staffed child and adolescent psychiatric services.

- 20 new posts in child psychology.

- The expansion of the home maker and home help services to assist families in difficulty.

- The establishment of "Community Mother" programmes in a number of health boards.

- Increased financial support for pre-school services in disadvantaged areas.

- 30 additional hostel places in Dublin for homeless youth.

- Making the Stay Safe child abuse prevention programme available to all primary schools.

The Government are committed to providing additional resources of a similar scale in each of the years 1994-96 and a provision for new developments costing £10m in a full year was included in 1994 Estimates. The developments which will occur over the next three years include:

- Better support services for vulnerable families which will be developed in conjunction with voluntary bodies.

- Improvements in the linkages between health boards, the Gardaí and schools in relation to the prevention and investigation of child abuse.

- Additional hostel places for homeless youth.

- New counselling and treatment services for children who have suffered abuse.

- Establishment of a system of supervision of pre-school services.

- Improvements in the availability of refuges and other services for victims of family violence.

- Increased supports for foster parents.

- Development of services, including specialised residential centres, to cater for disturbed and damaged children and adolescents.

- Staff development and training for those who will have responsibility for the operation of the legislation.

Action will also be taken on the recommendations of the Kilkenny Incest Report in relation to the preparation of new Child Abuse Guidelines, maintenance of child abuse registers and the conduct of case conferences. A Discussion Paper will be issued in 1994 on the question of providing for mandatory reporting by designated professionals of all forms of child abuse. This will form the basis of consultations with relevant interests with a view to achieving as much common ground as possible on mandatory reporting.

Adoption

Changes will be introduced in adoption law and procedure to:

- Provide arrangements to facilitate contact between adopted persons and their birth parents.

- Amend current legislation on the recognition of foreign adoptions to bring it into line with the recently agreed Hague Convention on the subject.

Travellers' health

A special programme will be implemented to address the particular health needs of the travelling community.

Primary healthcare for travellers is delivered in each health board area through the Community Care Programme and involves a co-ordinated multi-disciplinary approach by a number of professionals including Public Health Nurses, Area Medical Officers, Social Workers, Community Welfare Officers and General Practitioners in the GMS scheme.

Despite the special efforts made to deliver health services to meet the specific needs of the travelling community, factors such as transient lifestyle, poor sanitation and living conditions, high unemployment and generally poor health awareness continue to militate against real improvements in the health of travellers. Studies in recent years have clearly indicated that life expectancy and general health status among the travelling community are considerably lower than the population average. While many of the factors which give rise to this problem are outside the direct control of the health services there is scope for achieving considerable improvements in the health status of the travelling community through concerted health promotion and care initiatives.

The Minister for Health welcomes the establishment of the Task Force on the Travelling Community by the Minister for Equality and Law Reform. The Department of Health and the Task Force will undertake a joint study in 1994 on travellers' health with particular emphasis on access to appropriate health services. Following the completion of this study a number of initiatives will be undertaken including in the following areas:

- The development, in consultation with traveller groups, of a health education programme aimed specifically at travellers. This programme would incorporate homemaking skills, advice on nutrition, family planning, dental care, safety and consanguinity.

- The development of models of traveller participation in health promotion and prevention to ensure the health education programmes are delivered to maximum effect.

- Ensuring that health boards make special arrangements to encourage and permit travellers to avail of primary care services, in particular GP services, dental care, ante- and postnatal care, family planning, child immunisations and, where appropriate, hospital based services.

- Simplifying services under the GMS including eligibility, immunisation and general health records to ensure better continuity of care from one health board area to another.

- Liaising closely with other relevant statutory and voluntary agencies providing services to travellers to ensure better targeting of services.

The Task Force has indicated that on the basis of the joint study it will make recommendations regarding health policy for travellers. Following the report of the Task Force the Minister will publish a policy on travellers' health which will take account of these recommendations.

Addressing drug misuse

The Department of Health will help implement the Government's strategy on addressing misuse in conjunction with the organisations involved in the area. The strategy includes developing appropriate preventive, treatment and rehabilitation services.

The illicit use of drugs continues to be a problem. The Health Research Board estimates that there were 2,000 persons receiving treatment for drug misuse in Dublin in 1991. It is acknowledged that the number of drug misusers is in fact higher than this figure.

It is accepted internationally that to deal effectively with the problem of drug misuse, a strategy must be in place which encompasses measures to tackle both the supply of and demand for illicit drugs. The Government has developed such a strategy and has established a co-ordinating mechanism which includes all of the organisations involved in its implementation.

The Department of Health will continue to play its role in this strategy. Specifically, the Department will provide for the development of the appropriate preventive, treatment and rehabilitation services. This will involve:

- Primary prevention programmes in schools.
- Prevention targeted at selected groups.
- Dissemination of information through public campaigns.
- The provision of increased detoxification and rehabilitation facilities.
- Enhanced support for voluntary groups and for services at local level.
- The provision of at least four additional primary care clinics to service catchment areas in the Dublin area where harm reduction and assessment services will be provided to drug misusers.
- The involvement of general practitioners in the implementation of the methadone protocol.

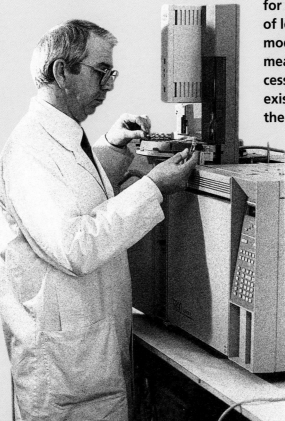

Food and medicine control

The Department of Health will update the legislative controls relating to food and medicine in Ireland. A national surveillance programme for controlling food-borne diseases will be developed and safe practices for the use of drugs and medicines will be further encouraged.

Food controls

Targets

To develop a national surveillance programme for the control of food-borne infections.

To meet EU obligations for the harmonisation of legislation and the modernisation of control measures and in the process to revise and update existing legislation, such as the Sale of Food and Drugs Acts and provisions under the Health Act, 1947.

To be achieved by:

- Establishing a new food unit in the Department of Health and a Food Safety Board.

Acute hospital services

- Upgrading food laboratory services.

- Achieving accreditation to international standards of the food laboratories designated for the purpose of EU directives.

- Conducting negotiations at EU level for new legislation and scientific co-operation.

- Guiding local management on their obligations for the enforcement of new controls.

Pharmacy and medicine controls

Target

To update the legal controls on pharmacy and medicines. To encourage rational and safe use of drugs and medicines.

To be achieved by:

- A new Pharmacy Act to consolidate existing legislation, to introduce more effective controls on the practice of pharmacy and to conform to current international standards.

- A new Medicines Act to update and expand the existing controls under the Sale of Food and Drugs Acts and the Health Act, 1947 and to have regard to our obligations as a member of the EU.

- The continuing emphasis on good quality prescribing by doctors.

- Public education programmes on the appropriate use of medicines.

The role of each acute hospital will be defined as part of a co-ordinated network of services delivering high quality care in the appropriate setting, in an equitable and cost-effective manner.

In the past, it has been argued that the acute hospital services have received a disproportionate emphasis both in status and resources as compared with other sectors of care. In line with the emphasis in the Health Strategy on providing appropriate care at the appropriate level, the hospital services must in future be perceived in terms of their role within the overall system.

Acute hospital services will continue to play a vital role in the provision of treatment but an appropriate balance will be struck between relying on the services in acute hospitals and the services that are and will be available in other settings. For example, the hospital should complement the role of the general practitioner as the first point of contact with the health services. In future, the acute hospital must be seen as but one part, albeit an important part, of a multi-functional and integrated healthcare system.

Many treatments and procedures which in former years required admission to hospital for a period of days can now be provided on a day-case basis. In 1987, some

85,000 patients or 15 percent of the total annual activity were treated on a day-case basis. By 1993, this figure had more than doubled to an estimated 176,000 which represented some 25 per cent of annual activity. This trend is expected to continue over future years and, taken together with other factors, is likely to have significant implications for the organisation and delivery of the acute hospital services, including the physical planning and operational policies of new or replacement facilities. In turn, these changes are likely to have an impact on the linkages between the acute hospital sector and other services.

Since the mid 1970s, successive Governments have addressed the need to streamline the acute hospital services in the light of changing needs. The appropriate shape of the hospital system is now broadly fitting into place. When the new hospital in Tallaght has been built and commissioned, the plan for acute hospital services in Dublin, which envisaged six major hospitals, will be in place. Further developments at these sites will be necessary.

Nationwide, the network of major regional hospitals will be completed with the provision of the new major regional facility at Ardkeen in Waterford. The new hospital in Sligo has recently been completed and a major refurbishment of the regional hospitals at Limerick and Galway is planned. Significant work is also being carried out at Cork Regional Hospital.

There is a strong network of general hospitals throughout the country and, while some of these are now based in new facilities, some work to up-grade and refurbish others will be required. The objective is to ensure quality facilities for patient care at all of these locations.

Developments over the past number of years at Letterkenny, Castlebar, Mullingar, Cavan, Wexford and Tralee have resulted in the most modern facilities being provided. It is intended to continue with a programme of upgrading and maintenance to ensure that all of the facilities in use provide high quality patient care.

The development of the acute hospital services over the next four years will thus be directed towards:

■ Providing a strong network of local and general hospitals which serve defined catchment areas and which will provide high quality hospital services for general medical and surgical facilities.

■ Providing a number of larger regional hospitals where more specialised services are available and which provide a broad range of regional specialities to the region they serve.

■ Providing a small number of highly specialised tertiary or supra-regional units which serve much wider catchment areas and concentrate resources nationally to the best effect.

■ Providing within each health board area a self-sufficiency in community and regional specialties.

■ As it is not feasible to develop a total comprehensive general hospital service on each acute hospital site, developing such a service within each health board area through a network of hospitals which will operate as a co-ordinated, complementary grouping. This will mean a precise determination of the role of each acute hospital as part of this grouping. It may also mean a redefinition of the existing roles of some hospitals.

■ Making the hospital service more responsive in the provision to general practitioners of an appropriate referral service; and, in association with this, examining the extent to which hospitals are used for services which should be provided by the general practitioner and developing measures to address this.

■ Bringing about a significant improvement in the quality of the ambulance service through the implementation of the report of the 1993 review group. The ambulance service will increasingly be seen as a pre-hospital service with strong ties to the acute general hospitals.

■ Continual development and testing of emergency plans, to which the acute hospital service is central, to ensure the most effective response when a major emergency occurs.

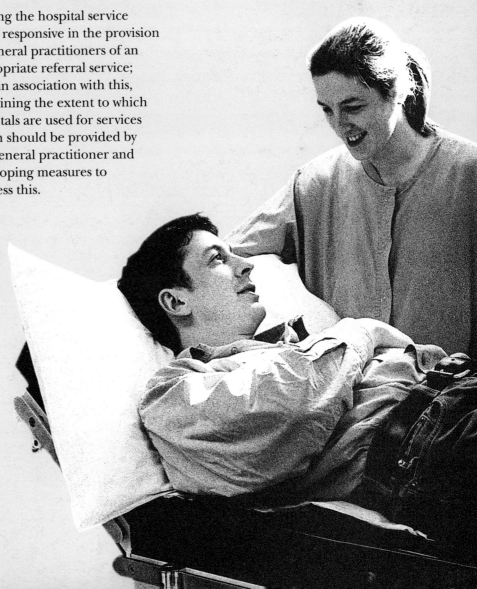

Equitable access

The coexistence of public and private practice within the public system must not undermine the principle of equitable access. For this reason, it was agreed in the context of the ***Programme for Economic and Social Progress*** to separate the two strands within the system, through the designation of specific beds for public and private patients, so as to achieve greater transparency. This system does not restrict the admission of patients who need emergency treatment, but ensures that private patients requiring elective procedures are admitted only to private beds. This in turn allows closer monitoring of the relative accessibility of the service to each category of patient and remedial action where necessary. The operation of this system will continue to be closely monitored.

Waiting lists are of particular concern in the context of equity. The Waiting List Initiative, which commenced in 1993 and continued in 1994, has had a marked effect in reducing waiting times for hospital treatment for public patients to acceptable levels and therefore in increasing equitable access. Between June and December 1993 the number of people awaiting admission to acute hospitals was reduced by 37 per cent, from over 40,000 to 25,000. Significant progress was made in reducing the waiting times for orthopaedics, ophthalmology and ear nose and throat (ENT) procedures. The Waiting List Initiative will be continued during 1994. The special allocation of £10m announced in the Budget will help make further progress in problem areas. A detailed review of the initiative is underway and the Department of Health will have discussions with health agencies on the most appropriate arrangements to put in place during 1994. The main objective will continue to be the elimination of waiting times of over 12 months for adults in the specialities with the largest problems and 6 months for children in the case of ENT and ophthalmology.

Safety of blood and blood products

All medical intervention carries some risks, which must be balanced against the benefits of the treatment concerned. Voluntary donations from blood donors play a major part in the successful treatment of thousands of patients each year, but the use of blood and blood products also carries some degree of risk.

Because of the critical importance of blood and blood products to our health services, the Minister for Health will continue to take whatever action is necessary to ensure the highest possible safety standards. He has established an expert group to report to him arising out of the infection of the Anti-D Immunoglobulin product manufactured by the Blood Transfusion Service Board. The report of the expert group will be acted upon urgently.

Cost-effectiveness

The technology and procedures within the acute hospital system will continue to be subject to rapid change. The approach to ensuring that these are geared to effectiveness and the best use of resources has been set out in detail in chapter two of the Health Strategy.

Cost-effectiveness is also determined by the efforts made by each hospital to obtain the best possible value in its varied expenditures.

In recent years the Department of Health has been intensifying its drive to improve value for money programmes throughout the services. The programmes have covered a wide range of items of expenditure such as purchases of medical and other supplies, insurance arrangements etc. A special Value for Money Unit in the Department of Health provides central direction for programmes and assists the agencies to co-operate in obtaining greater savings than might be possible were they operating in isolation from each other.

HIV/AIDS patients

The Chief Executive Officers of the health boards have established three Value for Money sub-committees, dealing with human resources, purchasing and good practice. These have enabled the health boards to work together in identifying and implementing opportunities for greater efficiency and for economy through co-operation.

While these efforts are not confined to the hospitals, this sector provides particular scope for savings because of the very high expenditure levels.

Over the next four years, it is intended to promote even greater co-operation between health agencies so that their very signif-icant joint buying power can be utilised, and effective practices can be transferred from one agency to another.

If Value for Money programmes are to be sustained, it is important that incentives are built into the system. Savings are more likely to be pursued vigorously by individual agencies and personnel if some element of the resources which are freed are then made available for approved service improvements in their own areas. Consideration will be given, in conjunction with the health agencies, to how incentives might best be applied so that efficient providers are rewarded and that the services ultimately benefit.

The Department of Health will implement a four-strand strategy on AIDS based upon surveillance, prevention, care and management and anti-discrimination.

HIV/AIDS statistics at end-1993 show that 378 people had developed AIDS of whom 182 had died. There were also 1,449 people who had been reported as being HIV positive It is generally accepted that this figure is understated. It is also clear that prevalence of HIV/AIDS continues to increase and that services will have to be developed to respond to this.

The Department of Health strategy is based on the recommen-dations of the National AIDS Strategy Committee and the Comhairle na nOspideal report on consultant services for HIV/AIDS patients. Because of the high incidence of intravenous drug abuse among those with AIDS or who are HIV positive the AIDS and drug abuse programmes are interlinked in many areas.

The strategy is concentrated on four main areas — surveillance, prevention, care and management and anti-discrimination. The AIDS strategy has the following objectives:

- To obtain a clearer picture of the prevalence of HIV infection in the community.

- To prevent the spread of HIV infection.

- To provide appropriate care and management at domiciliary, community and hospital level for those with HIV/AIDS.

- To ensure that persons with HIV/AIDS are not discriminated against.

Within the context of the Four-Year Action Plan the following action will be taken:

Ill and dependent elderly

Surveillance

- Maintain the existing linked testing programme and ensure the improved dissemination of information to Regional AIDS Co-ordinators by the end of 1994.

- Extend the existing unlinked anonymous surveillance programme on ante-natal bloods to sexually transmitted diseases (STD) clinics by the end of 1994.

- Introduce pilot unlinked anonymous HIV surveillance programmes on hospital out-patient attendances by the end of 1995.

- Continue to improve the reporting systems for AIDS cases and deaths during the period of the Plan.

Prevention

- Continue with and enhance the existing primary education programmes on HIV/AIDS

- Enhance risk-reduction pro-grammes aimed at specific groups. This will include the provision of additional satellite clinics for drug abusers as already indicated in the section on addressing drug misuse.

Care and management

- Develop domiciliary services for persons with AIDS.

- Provide additional respite facilities and services.

- Develop support structures to enable general practitioners and other community based personnel to provide appropriate care for HIV/AIDS sufferers.

- Phase in the recommendations of Comhairle na nOspideal on consultant services for AIDS patients. This will continue in 1994 with the recruitment of consultants in infectious diseases in the Eastern and Southern Health Boards and a consultant in palliative medicine in Dublin.

Anti-discrimination

The situation will be kept under review in consultation with other agencies to ensure that persons with HIV/AIDS are not discriminated against.

Priority will be given over the next four years to strength-ening home, community and hospital services to provide much-needed support to elderly people who are ill or dependent, and to assist those who care for them.

The rapid rise in the number of people in the oldest age groups poses a special challenge to health services in the next four years. Services in the community and in hospital will have to be responsive to the increased demand which this growing population of older people is likely to bring.

The objectives of health and personal social services for older people which currently guide the development of services were recommended in the Report of the Working Party on Services for the Elderly, *The Years Ahead — A Policy for the Elderly.* They are:

- To maintain older people in dignity and independence at home in accordance with the wishes of older people as expressed in many research studies.

- To restore to independence at home those older people who become ill or dependent.

■ To encourage and support the care of older people in their own community by family, neighbours and voluntary bodies in every way possible.

■ To provide a high quality of hospital and residential care for older people when they can no longer be maintained in dignity and independence at home.

In recent years services for ill and dependent elderly people have improved, in accordance with the recommendations of *The Years Ahead*. More nursing care and home help has been provided to support dependent elderly people living at home. Day care and respite facilities have been expanded providing support to families caring for an dependent older person at home. The number of specialist departments of medicine of old age attached to general hospitals has increased from eight in 1988 to eighteen this year. Long stay residential care has been reorganised and improved in many areas. The Health (Nursing Homes) Act 1990, which provides a new framework for the registration of nursing homes and for the payment of nursing home subventions, has been implemented. Health boards have also improved their co-ordination of services for older people and their carers. Voluntary organisations have played an important part in reorienting services for older people and in pioneering innovative ways of caring for older people and supporting their carers.

While considerable progress has been made in the past few years in improving services for ill and dependent older people, much remains to be done before the objectives of *The Years Ahead* are achieved.

Priority in the next four years will be given to:

■ Promoting healthy ageing, with the assistance of the National Council for the Elderly and in co-operation with the statutory and voluntary bodies involved with older people.

■ Strengthening the role of the general practitioner, the public health nurse, the home help and other primary care professionals in supporting older people and their carers who live at home. The target will be to ensure that not less than 90 per cent of those over 75 years of age continue to live at home.

■ Increasing the number of specialist departments of medicine of old age so that every general hospital either has such a department or has access to one.

■ Providing additional places for convalescent care for elderly people who do not need acute medical care.

■ Ensuring that adequate funding is available to meet in full the requirements of the Health (Nursing Homes) Act, 1990 by the end of 1996.

■ Providing eight small-scale nursing units in the community by the end of 1997 to replace unsuitable accommodation and to meet the needs of the expanding population of older people.

To provide the firmest possible basis for the planning of services in the longer-term, the Department of Health will commission a study on the implications for the health services of the projected increase in the elderly population over the next ten years.

Palliative care

Proper recognition will be given to the importance of palliative care for terminally ill patients, and the continued development of these services will be promoted in a structured manner.

The care of terminally ill people has improved significantly with the development of the hospice movement and the collaboration between the Irish Cancer Society and the health boards. While a central concern of the Health Strategy is to reduce the incidence of cancer, it is also very important to improve the quality of life of people with a terminal illness.

The objective of palliative care is to achieve the highest possible quality of life for both patient and family. Ireland has a strong tradition in this area, with hospices in Dublin and Cork that date from the late 1800s.

In recent years there have been significant increases in the number and variety of palliative care services including hospice units, home care teams (involving a growing network of palliative nurses in close liaison with general practitioners), day care services and services for terminally ill children. In addition, palliative care is now becoming available to people with forms of terminal illness other than cancer, such as Motor Neurone Disease. It is also being provided for people with AIDS.

The important role that palliative care services play in improving the quality of life of people with a terminal illness is acknowledged, and it is intended to promote the continued development of such services in a structured manner, making use where possible of existing health facilities. There will also be an emphasis on the role of general practitioners in developing appropriate palliative care services.

People with mental illness

Further progress will be made over the next four years in developing services for people with a mental illness or infirmity, in appropriate settings such as specialist departments in general hospitals, hostels and day centres in the community.

The objectives of the mental health services are:

- To promote mental health.
- To restore the mentally ill to as independent and normal a life as possible.

The services should provide care in a way that causes minimum disruption to the lives of the mentally ill and that of their families. The report, *Planning for the Future*, published in 1984 recommended how such objectives could be achieved. Its recommendations are still valid today, i.e. that mental health services should be:

- Comprehensive.
- Integrated with other health services.
- Based as far as possible in the community.
- Organised in sectors close to the people being served.

Reorganisation of services

The extent of the reform of the mental health services is documented in the *Green Paper on Mental Health* published in 1992 and in the *Annual Reports of the Inspector of Mental Hospitals*.

Substantial progress has been made in recent years in reorganising mental health services:

- Services have been transferred from large psychiatric hospitals to specialist departments in general hospitals. Of the 28,000 persons admitted for acute psychiatric treatment in 1992, more than one third were admitted to general hospitals.

- The number of people residing in psychiatric hospitals has fallen from 11,000 in 1984 to 6,000 at the end of 1992. Patients have been offered alternative accommodation in hostels in the community which now provide over 2,300 places and in hospitals and homes for the elderly and people with a mental handicap.

- Services in many parts of the country have been reorganised in sectors as recommended in *Planning for the Future*. This means that people with a mental illness can avail of services in mental health centres close to where they live, reducing the necessity in many cases of admission to hospital.

In view of these major changes in the organisation of mental health services, the Department will be supporting an important research project to evaluate the delivery of mental healthcare according to the principles of *Planning for the Future*. The research will be conducted simultaneously in a number of countries of the European Union and will provide valuable information on the effectiveness of mental healthcare for the long-term mentally ill.

Promoting mental health

Steps have also been taken to promote mental health, principally through support for the work of the Mental Health Association of Ireland, GROW, AWARE, the Schizophrenia Association of Ireland and other groups active in this field.

Suicide

An issue of growing concern for the mental health services is the increase in the rate of suicides, especially among young people. Although not all people who take their own lives suffer from a mental illness, the mental health service has a particular responsibility to prevent suicide. The Department and the Southern Health Board will be jointly funding a research project in 1994 and 1995 to assess the effect on the rate of suicide of more active intervention by the mental health services with those who attempt suicide. Depending on the outcome, further research may be necessary to assess the effectiveness of the methodology in other parts of the country; this will be undertaken if required.

Alcoholism

Admission rates to Irish psychiatric hospitals remain high. One reason is the high rate of admission for treatment of alcoholic disorders, which accounted for over 20 per cent of all admissions in 1991. While it became accepted practice in the past to admit people who were alcoholics to hospital, recent research has shown that treatment for the problem in the community is as effective as treatment in hospital. As part of the national policy on alcohol referred to earlier in this document, it will be the aim of the mental health services to encourage treatment for alcoholism on a non-residential basis, with the intervention of trained personnel in the community, in co-operation with general practitioners.

Legislation

The *Green Paper on Mental Health*, referred to above, analysed the shortcomings of current legislation in relation to the detention of people with mental disorder who require treatment in their own interest or in the interests of others. New safeguards are required to ensure confidence in the procedures for detention and to bring our legislation into conformity with the European Convention of Human Rights. Following the recent consultation with interested parties on the proposals for new legislation in the Green Paper, a White Paper containing proposals for new legislation is in preparation.

People with mental handicap

Priorities

Priorities for the further enhancement of services for people with a mental illness or infirmity over the next four years are:

- To promote mental health in co-operation with the voluntary mental health bodies.

- To provide departments of psychiatry in general hospitals. A further nine departments should open by 1997.

- To integrate mental health and primary health services and in particular to strengthen the role of general practitioners in the care of the mentally ill.

- To provide comprehensive specialist psychiatric services for children and adolescents in each health board.

- To develop specialist assessment and community support services in each health board for people suffering from dementia, including Alzheimer's disease, and their carers.

- To provide appropriate facilities for the care of the mentally ill whose behaviour is a risk to themselves or to others.

- To introduce a new Mental Health Act to give greater protection to the civil rights of the small number of people with a mental illness who have to be detained for treatment and to bring our legislation into conformity with the European Convention on Human Rights.

The development of appropriate residential and community — based facilities will continue, with a particular emphasis on catering for unmet need.

Policy on mental handicap services is based on the recommendations of the Review Group on Mental Handicap Services, *Needs and Abilities* (1990). The objective of the mental handicap service is to develop the person with mental handicap to the maximum of his/her potential.

The level of funding for services for persons with a mental handicap has increased very significantly since 1991. The annual allocation to these services has been increased cumulatively by £6 million in 1992, £8.5 million in 1993 and a further £12.5 million in 1994. Also in 1994, a capital programme will commence for the training of persons with a disability.

The additional funding has been used to provide more residential places for emergency and long-term care, day care and an expanded home care programme. However, there is still a level of unmet need which must be addressed. In addition, the increased longevity of persons with mental handicap results in changes in the type of need which must be met.

The number of people receiving residential services has been increased from 5,817 in 1988 to 6,582 in 1993. The number receiving day services has been increased from 5,219 to 6,817 in the same period. The information currently available indicates that there are still about 1,300 people waiting for residential services and 1,500 for day services. What is not clear from this information, however, is the proportion of those on waiting lists who require immediate placement and the level of care which they require. Nor does it indicate those who, with the provision of improved support services, could continue to live in the community.

The funding has also helped the programme of transferring to more appropriate settings those people with a mental handicap who have been accommodated in psychiatric hospitals. The number of such people was reduced from 1,432 in December 1990 to 942 in December 1992. 1993 data are not yet available.

The key developments that will be put in place over the next four years are as follows:

- The establishment of a national data base on the needs of people with mental handicap, to ensure that the services which are being provided meet the changing needs of the population of people with mental handicap and their families. The data base will:

People with physical/sensory handicap

■ Improve the accuracy of data available to health boards on the population of people with mental handicap.

■ Enable the current needs of clients with mental handicap to be assessed more accurately.

■ Support planning for the future development of services for clients.

■ Further expansion of residential and day places.

■ Provision of flexible home support schemes and respite care services. The introduction of the home support scheme in 1992 greatly enhanced the range of services available to people with mental handicap and their families. In particular it has enabled service providers to assist those families with no service or those receiving a service which does not fully meet the needs of the person with mental handicap. Over 3,000 clients and their families have benefited from this scheme and further funding will be provided in 1994 to enable the scheme to be extended.

■ Continuation of the programme to relocate people with a mental handicap who are currently in psychiatric hospitals to more appropriate care settings.

■ The development of a policy in 1994 for a service for people with mental handicap who have disturbed behaviour and its implementation on a phased basis.

■ Implementing the Department's policy document on services for people with autism which will be published in the coming months.

■ Providing Hepatitis B vaccination for staff working in the mental handicap services and client groups who are considered to be at risk.

■ Helping to reduce the incidence of mental handicap by providing genetic counselling services. A new medical genetic counselling service is being established at Our Lady's Hospital, Crumlin, and will be supported by a medical genetic laboratory service also based at that hospital.

Services for people with a physical or sensory handicap will be further developed on the basis of locally assessed need.

A Review Group is currently examining the health service needs of people with a physical or sensory disability and will report during 1994. On foot of an Interim Report by the Review Group, an additional £1.5 million was provided in 1993 for service developments. This is being maintained in the annual funding, and a further £1.5 million has been made available in 1994.

The Wider Dimension

This additional funding has supported a number of important developments including the provision of additional residential places and the development of community care services such as the care attendant scheme and speech therapy, physiotherapy and occupational therapy.

It is intended to build on the progress which has been made. The emphasis will be on providing extra facilities on the basis of locally assessed need. The main focus in the coming four years, subject to the recommendations of the Review Group on Physical and Sensory Disability, will be:

- To provide extra facilities for day care, respite care, home care and personal support services, and residential care/ independent living.

- To provide additional residential facilities for the young chronic sick.

- To improve the organisation and co-ordination of services.

- To build up information on the service needs of clients — this will be facilitated by the establishment of a national database on physical handicap.

- To employ additional occupational therapists, speech therapists and physiotherapists.

- To improve the counselling and psychological support services for people with disabilities and their families.

- To improve vocational training standards and facilities with a view to greater economic integration of people with a disability in society.

- To address the funding base for voluntary bodies who provide services and support to persons with a physical/sensory disability.

- To improve the availability of technical aids and appliances.

In addition to these improvements in services, steps will also be taken to help reduce the incidence of Neural Tube Defects (NTDs) by increasing the awareness among women of child-bearing age of the need to have adequate folic acid in their diet.

The Health Strategy has set out targets for achieving measurable improvements in selected priority areas. Many of these may be achieved by action within the health sector, but others are reliant on the involvement of agencies outside the health sphere.

The dimensions outside the immediate health area must therefore be recognised. They will have a growing influence on the achievement of health gain and social gain.

The multi-sectoral dimension

The importance of seeing health as an issue affected by public policy in many other areas will continue to be emphasised. To this end a key function of the Minister and Department of Health will be to ensure that all other sectors take the health implications of their own policies and practices fully into account. This is in keeping with the approach set out in *Health — The Wider Dimensions* (published in 1986) and the 1987 document *Promoting Health through Public Policy*. It is also reflected in Article 129 of the Maastricht Treaty.

The activities of many public bodies outside the immediate health field affect our health. These include:

- Department of the Environment, the county councils and corporations.

- Environmental Protection Agency.

- National Safety Council.

- National Authority for Occupational Safety and Health.

- National Irish Safety Organisation.

- Department of Agriculture, Food & Forestry.

- Department of Finance.

- Department of the Marine.

- Departments of Education and Enterprise & Employment (for promoting healthy lifestyles and educating and training people with disabilities and ensuring health and safety in the workplace).

- Department of Justice and the Customs and Excise (drug abuse).

It is worth stressing that the responsibility for ensuring that these activities are properly provided with public health in mind rests with these agencies. The task of the health sector is:

- To act as the guardian of the public health interest; and

- To encourage those outside the health sector to appreciate the health significance of their actions.

The Department of Health will arrange regular inter-departmental meetings in order to ensure that the health implications of policies formulated by other public bodies are fully assessed.

The EU dimension

The targets in this Strategy take account of developments in the European Union. Until recently the EU had no formal competence in the field of public health, although a substantial body of health controls dealing with food, medicines and cosmetics had been introduced as part of the creation of a Single European Market. The EU had also been active in a number of areas such as AIDS, drug dependence, cancer, nutrition, alcohol abuse and health education. However, the Maastricht Treaty contains a new article (Art. 129) giving the EU a formal involvement in health measures.

The Treaty provides the first formal opportunity for the development in the Union of a coherent and active public health policy. Article 129 states that:

"The Community shall contribute toward ensuring a high level of human health protection by encouraging co-operation between the Member States, and if necessary, lending support to their action. Community action shall be directed towards the prevention of diseases, in particular the major health scourges, including drug addiction, by promoting research into their causes and their transmission, as well as health information and education"

The emphasis of the new Article is on assisting co-operation between member states, and such co-operation will complement the steps announced in this Strategy. The European Commission has set out its proposals for a *Framework for Action in the Field of Public Health* under Article 129. It sets out a strategy for action, identifies the means available to the Union to accomplish its aims and establishes the procedures for evaluation, review and consultation.

The document provides an overview of the main health-related problems and challenges facing member states today. They include:

- The ageing population of the Union.

- Increasing population mobility into the Union and between Member States.

- Changes in the environment and in the work place.

- Rising expectations about what health services can and should deliver.

- The general socio-economic problems of the Union.

The role of the Union is to underpin the efforts of the member states in the public health field, to assist in the formulation and implementation of objectives and strategies and to contribute to the continuity of health protection provision across the Union. This will be achieved in particular by promoting the exchange of experience and views and the establishment of liaison arrangements for the monitoring and control of diseases.

The Commission has identified a number of areas for priority action in the future. These are:

- Health promotion, education and training.

- Health data and indicators, and monitoring and surveillance of diseases.

- Cancer.

- Drug misuse.

- AIDS and other communicable diseases.

- Intentional and unintentional accidents and injuries.

- Pollution-related diseases.

- Rare diseases.

It will be a matter for the Council of Ministers to take the final decisions both in relation to the areas for priority action and on the specific actions to be taken.

During the discussions on the Maastricht Treaty, Ireland proposed that health protection under Article 129 should form an explicit part of the Union's other policies. This was accepted by our EU partners. It means that issues which affect health, such as the quality of the environment and agricultural production, can be linked to health promotion. This linkage offers an important opportunity to develop co-operation between EU countries to tackle the main causes of preventable illness.

The WHO dimension

In addition to agencies outside the health sector, Ireland has maintained close links with the World Health Organisation. The WHO has a particularly important role in promoting the multi-sectoral aspect of health and this Strategy underpins that approach. The targets set in this Strategy are influenced by the WHO's *Health for All* targets. The Strategy is also influenced by the six main underlying themes of the WHO programme:

- Promotion of equity.

- Health promotion and prevention of disease.

- Development of active participation.

- Multi-sectoral co-operation.

- Focus on primary healthcare.

- Development of international co-operation.

North/South co-operation

In addition to the links at international level, there is also an important element of North-South co-operation on health matters in Ireland. There are significant benefits in the area of joint purchasing of supplies and in the provision of services at a supra-regional level. Co-operation is also of obvious value in relation to joint approaches to health promotion. Important initiatives have been taken in this area in the fields of immunisation, lifestyle, alcohol programmes and AIDS. There is a continuing exchange of information on topics such as smoking, fitness and health, cancer education, cancer screening and mental health legislation. North-South co-operation was an important dimension to the celebration of the European Year of Older People. Apart from the above initiatives, which mainly centre on the Department of Health in the Republic and the Department of Health and Social Services in Northern Ireland, there is also co- operation at the level of the individual health board. This is particularly the case with adjoining boards (the North-Eastern and North-Western Health Boards in the Republic, and the Southern and Western Health and Social Services Boards in Northern Ireland). The potential for further co-operation, both centrally and at board level, will be fully explored.